D1139167

COUNTDOWN!
or How Nigh is the End?

Patrick Moore
COUNTDOWN!
or How Nigh is the End?

MICHAEL JOSEPH/RAINBIRD

To Caroline Zubaida, with thanks for all her
help and encouragement – without which I doubt whether
the book would have seen the light of day.

First published in Great Britain in 1983
by Michael Joseph Limited
44 Bedford Square, London WC1B 3DU and
The Rainbird Publishing Group Limited
40 Park Street, London W1Y 4DE
who designed and produced the book

ISBN 0 7181 2291 7

Illustrations by Paul Doherty

Text set by Wyvern Typesetting Ltd, Bristol, England
Printed and bound by Mackays of Chatham Limited,
Chatham, Kent, England

Contents

Introduction

A few months ago I was walking along Charing Cross Road, in Central London, when I came across a man who was wearing sandwich-boards. Normally I would have paid little attention to him, and I would have assumed that he must have been protesting about something quite mundane, but in fact his message was much more dramatic: 'Sinners Repent. The Hour of Doom is at Hand!' I was tempted to question him, but at that moment he stepped off the kerb and was smartly knocked down by a passing cyclist. Rising to his feet, he drew a deep breath and unloosed a volley of lurid invective. He went on speaking for at least five minutes, saying something different all the time; and had I approached him with a mild query, he would undoubtedly have thrown his sandwich-boards at me. Therefore I considered discretion to be the better part of valour, and went on my way.

Actually, end-of-the-world prophets of this kind are much less common than they used to be, which is perhaps a pity; the world would be a duller place without its Independent Thinkers, as I have called them. But they still exist, and there are other types of doomsday prophets as well. Some of them are purely religious; others fear that we may be blasted out of space by a collision with a comet, an asteroid or even a passing star; yet others maintain that the end of civilization, if not of the world itself, will be brought about by the evil machinations of alien beings in flying saucers. I cannot pretend to be particularly apprehensive, except of the real possibility that some politician will press the wrong button and spark off a nuclear war which would certainly eliminate the human race. And yet the Earth will not last for ever; nothing in the universe is eternal – perhaps not even the universe itself. Our world came into being because of the Sun, and in the end the Sun will destroy it.

I do not want to sound alarmist. The Sun, fortunately for us, is a steady, well-behaved star, and even though it may have fluctuated sufficiently to produce the various Ice Ages (the last of which ended a mere 10,000 years ago) it is not likely to change much in the foreseeable future. Indeed, it will not alter for at least 5,000 million years as yet, and probably rather longer, so that there is no immediate need for us to pack our bags and start searching for a planet safer than ours. We have a long respite, and if we refrain from blowing each other up we may well hope to find a solution before the crisis comes.

However, end-of-the-world seers are still with us, and some of them are ready to give their reasons in great detail. In this book, I want to look at the various theories and try to decide whether or not they are valid. It is a fascinating subject, and it will take us from the realms of astrology and mysticism right through to pure astronomy. I hope that you will enjoy it – and let me say at once that in my view, at least, you will have ample time to read these pages before anything traumatic happens to the world which is our home. If I am wrong, please accept my apologies in advance.

Chapter One

William Miller – and Others

The year was 1843. A brilliant comet blazed down from the sky, 'shaking its fiery locks'. There was great tension in America, and there were thousands of people who believed that the Last Trump was about to sound. This was the time of the Millerite movement, which led to one of the greatest end-of-the-world scares ever known. It was centred in the United States, though traces of it spread further afield, and were slow to fade away. The whole episode had been sparked off by a New England farmer named William Miller.

Miller was not a scientist; he was a student of the Bible, and he was eccentric. Indeed, it is not too much to say that he was as nutty as a fruit-cake; but he had a tremendous following, and he was completely sincere. To him, the Second Coming of Christ was imminent, and he regarded it as his bounden duty to spread the word among his fellow men – in which he succeeded only too well, aided and abetted by a clergyman named Joshua V. Hines, who acted as his publicity agent and who fanned the flames with uncanny skill.

I have started this chapter with William Miller because his crusade of doom was so incredibly successful. Even when the fateful year of 1843 was over, the Millerite movement did not perish abruptly; it petered out slowly, and echoes of it lingered on. However, it is best to deal with matters chronologically, and so let us delve back much further than the 19th century to see what we can find out.

I do not propose to say much about ancient religions, because they do not really come into the story, and in any case most of them regarded the Earth as eternal. (The same was true of the gods, with the notable exception of those in Norse mythology; you may remember that in the final battle between the Æsir and the forces of evil, the chief god Odin was unceremoniously swallowed by the wolf Fenrir – which was unfortunate for Odin, and may well have given Fenrir indigestion.) So we really begin with St Augustine, who is always remembered as being the man sent to England to convert the inhabitants to Christianity. In this he had considerable success, starting with King Ethelbert of Kent. To be candid, history has been rather kind to Augustine; he came to England with marked reluctance, and his lack of tact very nearly ruined the entire mission. Still, he made his mark, and he was certainly forceful.

Augustine lived in the sixth and seventh centuries AD, and his meeting with King Ethelbert took place in the year 596. Apparently he believed that the Church would last for 1,000 years but no longer, and this paved the way for the first of the religious end-of-the-world scares. If Christ had been born in AD 1, then presumably the year 1000 would complete the cycle. Druthmar, an English monk, even gave a definite date: 24 March – and the stage was set.

Experts in religious history will see a flaw here at once, because whenever Christ was born, it was certainly not in AD 1.* All the evidence indicates that Christ was born in or near 4 BC, though we cannot be certain of anything, and all dates in this period are somewhat arbitrary. However, the approach of AD 1000 was dreaded in every country to which Christianity had penetrated – and this, of course, included England, though the panics were even greater in Italy, France and what is now Germany.

It was, incidentally, a peculiarly unpleasant time for most people. Warfare was widespread, and in addition Europe was in the grip of one of those plagues which have been prevalent every now and then. Many victims may well have thought that the forthcoming end of the world would be a relief rather than otherwise. The Church did not agree, and much money and effort was spent in erecting new

---

*Note, please, that there is no year 0; we go straight from 1 BC to AD 1, which complicates matters still further. At that time the most powerful man in the European world was Augustus, ruler of Rome; he was Julius Cæsar's great-nephew, and had come to power after ousting Mark Antony, who had been too preoccupied with wooing Cleopatra to give his attention to more pressing matters. Augustus is also memorable for having upset the calendar merely because he wanted August, the month named in his honour, to be as long as Cæsar's month, July; this is why we now have two consecutive months with 31 days each.

cathedrals and renovating old ones — the basic idea being, presumably, that those who were busy upon such noble projects would be given V.I.P. treatment when the world was no more. The English were having extra problems, since Ethelred the Unready sat upon the throne, and the Danish raids were increasing all the time. Ethelred was completely unprepared for them, and it is permissible to think that he would have been equally unprepared for the end of the world, but the matter was never actually put to the test, because nothing happened. The year 1000 came in, passed by, and expired without any divine manifestations whatsoever. It must have been rather galling for the thousands of Christians, mainly from continental Europe, who had sold up all their possessions in 999 and made haste to Jerusalem, where the Second Coming might logically have been expected.

The fears of AD 1000 were decidedly nebulous, and were based upon a mere time-scale rather than anything specific in the Bible. Much later came a Spaniard, St Vincent Ferrer, who was born in or about 1350 and died in 1419. He concluded that the world would last for as many years as there are verses in the Psalms. As there are 2,357 verses, there seemed no reason for apprehension.

To catalogue all the individual prophets who forecast Doomsday on purely religious grounds would take a long time, and would be rather tedious, but I cannot resist saying something about Solomon Eccles, partly because he was English and partly because he was so odd by any standards. He seems to have been born in London in 1618, and his early career was conventional enough; he was a talented musician, and when still in his twenties he was making a good living by teaching stringed and keyboard instruments. Later he fell in with the Quakers, and began to have visions which told him quite plainly that the end was nigh. Music, of course, was a pastime of the Devil, so he disposed of all his equipment and became a shoemaker. This in itself would have aroused no comment, but he also disposed of his clothing (or most of it; at first he retained a loincloth to cover the appropriate part of his anatomy) and began to burst in upon religious services, imploring the congregations to take heed and be saved while there was still time. It was hardly surprising that preachers did not take kindly to this sort of interruption, and the usual result was that Eccles was thrown out, metaphorically upon his ear. He was even imprisoned, which apparently troubled him not at all.

His strange career approached its zenith, so far as London was concerned, in the years of plague and fire, 1665 and 1666. No doubt he regarded these events as warnings of the holocaust to come. He even attracted the attention of the great diarist Samuel Pepys, who wrote in 1667: 'One thing extraordinary was, this day a man, a Quaker, came naked through the Hall at Westminster, where all the courtiers assembled, only civilly tied about the loins to avoid scandal, and with a chafing-dish of fire and brimstone up in his head did pass through the Hall at Westminster crying "Repent! Repent!"'

Since the stupid Londoners refused to take him seriously, Eccles decided to venture elsewhere; he went to Scotland, and was arrested again. On his release he made for Ireland, where he regarded even a loincloth as an unnecessary encumbrance. Yet he met with no better fortune, and when he streaked naked into Cork Cathedral during a solemn service both the Church and the civil authorities were outraged. He was whipped through the streets, and then expelled from the city with stern warnings never to come back.

He did join a Quaker missionary party to the West Indies in 1671, and then went to New England, where he was at once arrested and subsequently banished. Nine years later we find him in Barbados, speaking to gatherings of Negro slaves; the authorities intervened and shipped him back to England, where he died.

Eccles does not seem to have selected any particular part of the Bible to bolster up his views. He relied upon his instinct and his visions, which is always a risky thing to do; and though he achieved considerable notoriety, he never mustered a following in the way that William Miller managed to do later.

In London, the next important prophet of doom was the Rev. Dr William Whiston, sometime friend of Newton; but since Whiston's theory involved a comet, I propose to defer its discussion for the moment and pass on to the year 1761, when the City was shaken by a couple of earthquakes. Both were very mild, and there was little damage, though a few chimneys were toppled and the shocks were strong enough to be noticeable. They are relevant here only because they led to a noteworthy panic, due entirely to the ravings of an ex-soldier whose name was William Bell.

It is often thought that earthquakes in England are uncommon, but this is not strictly true; a thousand have been recorded altogether, though only one death has been established – in 1580, when a moderate shock dislodged a stone from Christ Church and deposited it upon the head of a luckless youth who happened to be standing underneath.* In 1761 the jolts were separated by 28 days, and Bell jumped to the conclusion that after another 28 days there would be something much worse – enough, in fact, to destroy the world. He gave the date as 5 April, and for reasons which remain a total mystery people believed him. Panic broke out, and spread through wide areas of London. A general exodus began; carts and coaches drew out of the City, and camps sprang up in regions which have now been swamped by the spread of London but were then pleasant villages, such as Highgate and Hampstead. Boats were bought up, and the Thames was crowded, presumably because it was thought that water would be safer than dry land.

Bell became famous; everything he said was magnified out of all proportion, and by the time that 5 April came the scene was one of utter chaos. Predictably, the day passed quietly, and there was a sense as much of anti-climax as of relief. Bell's enthusiasm for his cause was not dampened, but the authorities had had more than enough, and the luckless ex-soldier was quietly stored in the nearest asylum, where he died some days later. It was a curious episode in every way, and there was no logic behind it.

I can pause only briefly to mention a lady named Mary Bateman, who achieved fame in 1806 when she announced that one of her hens was making a habit of laying eggs with Jesus Christ's personal seal upon them; clearly, this meant that the Second Coming and the end of the world were imminent. Unfortunately it was found that the eggs had been skilfully treated by Mary herself, so that Christ was not involved. It was, in fact, a pure confidence trick, and Mrs Bateman's subsequent career was no more creditable; it came to an abrupt end after she had been caught giving two wealthy clients a tasty-looking pudding which had been liberally laced with arsenic.

There was also John Tom, a Cornishman who called himself Sir William Percy Honeywood Courtney, and actually stood twice for

---

*The most violent English quake ever recorded shook the Colchester area on 22 April 1884, at 9.18 a.m. There were two sharp jolts which damaged over 1,000 buildings, and in the village of Abberton only six chimneys were left intact. I have felt two earthquakes myself, one in Shrewsbury and the other in my home village of Selsey, though on each occasion I admit that I had no idea what they were, and put them down to passing lorries.

Parliament. He fought the Canterbury constituency in 1832, and collected 375 votes, which was 372 more than he managed at his second attempt some years later. Eventually he announced that he was the new Messiah, and that he had been sent to give news of the impending destruction of the Earth. Courtney, too, came to an untimely end after he shot a policeman who had been ordered to break up a mob which he had collected and was leading along the road from London to Dover.

We are used to curious Parliamentary candidates. They crop up at every election, and some of them are successful; you have only to look at the present House of Commons to see how true this is. However, Tom (or should we say Sir William?) was really a little too much, and the citizens of Canterbury were no doubt wise in preferring one of the conventional, albeit dreary, politicians of the kind still boring us today.

And so, at last, let us return to that greatest of all prophets of doom: William Miller.

Judged by any standards, Miller was a phenomenon. His background was quite normal; he was born in Pittsfield, Massachusetts, and his parents were farmers in a modest way. They were also Baptists, which was admittedly harmless. William's only sign of eccentricity was that he was an avid reader who devoured any book he could find, which was by no means common at the time. When he and his family moved to the state of Vermont, he became known as a young man of learning, and he was elected Constable of the town of Poultney; in 1809 he was even made Sheriff, and clearly he was cast in a different mould from most of his contemporaries. He married, and at that stage was by no means of a religious turn of mind. He went so far as to declare that the Bible was nonsense, an attitude which horrified his parents.

Meanwhile, storm-clouds were gathering, and war against the English was more than probable. Miller decided to serve his country, and so he joined the army. In 1810 he was commissioned, and by 1812 he held the rank of captain. He saw plenty of action, but he also met with an accident which probably changed the whole course of his life. The exact details of the mishap are unknown, but involved a fall from a cart, and the fact that Miller landed on his head may well have been the root cause of his transformation from an energetic, practical man into a fanatical end-of-the-worlder. We will never know. However, the change was not immediately obvious, and he stayed in the army until 1815, when he resigned his commission and established a farm at Low Hampton, which was then a remote part of New York State.

It was at Low Hampton that Miller found God – or thought he had. His life style changed entirely, and he began to spend more and more time reading the Bible, particularly the Book of Daniel. The walls of his study were festooned with charts and graphs, and he became more or less a recluse. Eventually he decided that the Second Coming of Christ was nearer than most people imagined, and would signal the end of the world as we know it. What of the date? By 1832 he had the answer; the world would be destroyed in 1843, probably at midnight at the spring equinox on 21 March.

At first he was cautious. Should he announce the dread news, or wait until the Earth was snuffed out like a candle-flame in the wind? To say nothing might be more merciful. On the other hand, there was plenty of sin around (though no doubt much less than there is today), and it would be only right to give the sinners time to repent so that they could face their Maker with confidence and a bright smile. Moreover, there were other prophets who were giving wrong dates. (One was a certain Harriet Livermore, whose career is decidedly obscure, but who expected the Last Trump to sound sometime in 1847. Another was a Captain Saunders, and yet a third was Joseph Wolff, who lived appropriately in Jerusalem, and who held the same opinion. Wolff expected Christ to appear on top of the Mount of Olives. One of his followers was Lady Hester Stanhope, a niece of William Pitt, who subsequently repaired to the top of the Mount taking two white horses with her – one for Jesus and the other for herself.)

Eventually Miller made up his mind. He must spread the word, and there were only a few years left. In 1832 be began his campaign by preaching in the local church. From all accounts, he was an excellent orator of the Hitler variety, and he was certainly positive. The end was nigh, he thundered; those who had led evil lives must make full atonement before it was too late, or they would be cast down into the flames of hell. It was a depressing prospect.

At first his success was modest. Some of the locals took him seriously, while others dismissed him as a crazy old man. What may have helped him was the great meteor shower of 1833 when, for some hours, shooting-stars 'rained down like snowflakes', indicating divine displeasure. Nowadays we know that the shower was due to the meteors known as Leonids; periodically the Earth plunges through the main swarm of tiny particles, scooping up many of them. There have been other comparable Leonid displays since, the last being in 1966. But to Miller, it was a sign that he was thinking along the right lines.

Gradually his fame spread. Over the following years he preached almost 1,000 sermons, and when challenged by sceptics he was able to give as good as he got; so far as the Bible was concerned he had done his homework extremely well, and of his sincerity there was no doubt at all. The Millerite sect became firmly established, and the year 1843 was awaited with considerable apprehension. It was at this juncture that Miller met up with a man who was destined to play a major role in the whole episode – the Elder Joshua V. Hines, a Baptist who had considerable influence in the city of Boston.

Hines is something of an enigma. While Miller was an honest fanatic, Hines was more of what we might call a 'con-man'. He may or may not have believed in the approaching holocaust; on the whole it seems that he didn't, but in any event he decided to appoint himself Miller's business manager. He invited him to preach at the Chardon Street Baptist Chapel in Boston, and hundreds of people turned up. The meeting was an outstanding success, and Miller followed it with more sermons throughout the following week. Hines organized things with consummate skill, and placards and advertisements began to appear, together with the inevitable men wearing sandwich-boards (shades of the Charing Cross Road!). Next came a series of meetings in Portsmouth, New Hampshire, where the results were much the same. The Millerites gained ground every day, and Joshua Hines resigned his official position as preacher in order to devote all his time to the movement. He even founded a paper, *Signs of the Times*, in which the message was given in unmistakable terms. Whether any issues of this periodical survive I do not know; I have been unable to locate any, but during the peak of Millerism it was all the rage.

Even New York was not immune. Wall Street and sky scrapers lay in the future, but plenty of people lived there, and Miller descended upon the city like an east wind, bellowing out his warnings and exhorting all sinners to repent. Whether New York had more than its fair share of sinners is open to question, but at this stage there were many Millerites who had sold all their belongings and joined in the crusade, firmly convinced that the Lord was about to swoop down from above and remove the Earth from the universe together with everybody in it.

Things were not helped by the appearance of a brilliant comet which dominated the night sky and caused a great deal of alarm and despondency. It was now 1843, and the Millerite movement was at its zenith; it did not even matter that William himself was ill with fever and had temporarily withdrawn from the scene. As the spring equinox approached, hysteria took over. On the evening of 21 March there was a general exodus from Boston, presumably because the Lord would be more likely to descend in open country than in a city, with the attendant danger of being impaled upon a chimney-stack or something equally inconvenient. Alas, nothing happened, but stirring events were taking place elsewhere. In the town of Westford, Massachusetts, hundreds of Millerites had assembled, and when they heard the sound of a trumpet they were naturally convinced that the end had come at last. Several people fainted before it was discovered that the trumpet call had been given by a local drunk, who had a perverted sense of humour and who had become thoroughly tired of being kept awake at night by the sounds of chanting and praying.

The world was still intact when 22 March dawned. There had been quite a number of casualties, including one man who had attempted a flight to Heaven by fitting himself with artificial wings and jumping out of a top-storey window — with the predictable result that he broke an arm. (According to some sources, this happened during the later stages of the scare rather than at the spring equinox itself, but the episode seems to be true.) The Millerites were not too depressed; 1843 still had many months to run, and it was too early to change course. Hines and his campaign managers continued the battle, and as the year drew to its end the hysteria was almost as great as ever. The panic had spread far and wide, and on 31 December a huge crowd gathered outside William Miller's house, no doubt anxious to receive the latest bulletins from on high. Still nothing happened. But Miller was not downhearted; suddenly he discovered a mistake in his predictions — they should have referred to the Jewish year, which was not due to end until 22 October 1844.

Clearly this was a serious blunder, but it could be put down to human fallibility, and the situation remained much as before. According to contemporary records, there were more than average numbers of admissions to lunatic asylums, and still the Millerites preached and thundered. Once more the crowds gathered. Once more, to their chagrin, the Lord refused to oblige. Miller made one more attempt; the end would come, he said, on the seventh day of the seventh month – but when this too passed without incident, he gave up. Joshua Hines retired from the arena (he lived to the age of ninety), and the Millerite movement faded away, with its members returning to their homes and doing their best to pick up the threads.

William Miller himself died soon afterwards. At least he had made his mark, and he never recanted; all that was wrong, he maintained, was the time-scale. To him, the Book of Daniel was infallible. Probably he regretted that he had not been more accurate, but there was nothing that he could do about it – he did not even show any marked desire to saddle up a third white horse and accompany Lady Hester Stanhope to Jerusalem.

To the best of my knowledge, 'Second Coming', end-of-the-world predictions have been confined mainly to the United States. Miller's was by far the most notable, but there have been several since, one of which was sparked off in 1925 by two people: a Los Angeles girl, Margaret Rowan, and a German-born housepainter whose name was Robert Reidt. It was centred in California, and never spread further. Neither did it affect thousands of people, as the Millerite movement had done, but I feel that I ought to mention it, because it is recent enough to be remembered by many people. (I do not remember it myself, but as I was then at the early age of two, and lived in Bognor Regis, this is hardly surprising.) Reidt was based at Patchogue on Long Island, and his predictions were entirely Biblical. He gave the date of doom as 13 February, and so did Margaret Rowan – on the authority, she said, of no less a person than the Archangel Gabriel, who was presumably in an excellent position to know. The Messiah would appear in the eastern sky, in the form of a small cloud. He would draw closer, and on arrival would scorch the world to a crisp, wafting the faithful to Heaven while the sinners (that is to say, the bulk of the population) would be left to fend for themselves in the equivalent of Dante's Inferno.

Eyes were turned skywards on 6 February, when the Messiah was due to make his entry. However, the anticipated cloud failed to materialize, and by the 13th the Messiah was still an absentee. Both Margaret Rowan and Robert Reidt claimed that he had been detained for some reason or other, and would be along shortly, but the few hundred followers began to show signs of discontent, and gradually drifted away. What happened to the two prophets does not seem to be known, but at any rate nothing more was heard from them.

Next came the Rev. Charles G. Long, of Pasadena, who returned to the Book of Daniel. (This seems to be a favourite end-of-the-world text, though most people will remember it better for its description of a slight *contretemps* involving lions.) Long decided that the end would come at 5.33 p.m., Pacific Time, on 21 September 1945. He founded a sect calling itself the Remnant of the Church of God, and for some years he preached away, gaining a few converts but failing to make much of an impact upon a world which was much more concerned with Adolf Hitler and the warlords of Japan. Seven days before the expected end, Long and his followers gave up eating (which was bearable) and drinking (which, under the circumstances, probably was not), and made their preparations. When 5.33 came and went, they gave resigned sighs and went back to their normal humdrum existence.

Finally, in this admittedly very incomplete catalogue, I come to May 1954. This time the seat of activity was not America, but Rome, the Eternal City, where the Colosseum stands. According to legend, the world will come to an end when the Colosseum falls. When cracks suddenly started to appear in the fabric of the amphitheatre, people became alarmed. For some reason that I have been unable to discover, 24 May was regarded as D-day, and there was a noticeable panic in which many Romans endeavoured to allay their fears by means of alcohol. Not to put too fine a point on it, they became as drunk as newts. The Pope was not impressed, and went so far as to issue an official denial. This had a calming effect; the Colosseum still stands: the end of the world has not come yet.

What are we to make of all this?

Without wishing to be irreligious, it is true to say that the Bible can be interpreted to mean almost anything provided that you are prepared to abandon all logic; it is merely a matter of taking passages out of context and stringing them together. (I remember a schoolboy essay in which it was shown, by means of perfectly correct quotes, that St Peter must have been a scratch golfer.) I do not think that any more 'Second Coming' stories of such a kind will gain much of a foothold today, and the biblical prophets of doom belong to the past. Of course, you never know, but it seems unlikely that anyone in AD 1983 will dream of riding to Jerusalem on a white horse to meet the Creator. I would not consider trying it myself (even if I were capable of riding anything more ambitious than a bicycle), and I doubt whether anyone else will try it either.

Chapter Two

The Astrologers

Not very long ago I had a letter from the secretary of a university students' union, inviting me to give a lecture. This, frankly, is nothing new; but I was intrigued by this one, because the writer asked whether I would be prepared to 'deliver a talk on the latest research in astrology'. What he meant was, of course, astronomy; it is incredible how 'in this day and age', to use one of those irritating 1983-type expressions, anyone can confuse the two. I was about to send a somewhat terse reply when I looked more carefully at the notepaper heading, and realized that the invitation came from a left-wing political group. This altered my attitude at once. Students of politics can hardly be expected to tell science from pseudo-science, and I rather unkindly referred the writer to the craziest astrologer I knew. I gather that the lecture was duly given, with interesting results!

I mention astrology here because it is very closely linked with end-of-the-world prophecies, and there have been several major panics, much the greatest being that of 1524, due directly to an eminent astrologer named Johann Stöffler. But before going any further, it is, I feel, essential to say something about astrology itself.

Basically, it is the superstition of the sky. Your character and destiny are supposed to depend upon the positions of the Sun, Moon and planets at the time of birth, so that, for instance, if you happen to have been born in London on 8 May you will be entirely different from a colleague who first saw the light of day on 7 September in Manchester. If I may be allowed to add a personal note: I made my entry on 4 March 1923, which means that my astrological sign is Pisces, the Fishes. I am therefore supposed to be gentle, kind, retiring, unlucky and often melancholy; I ought to spend much of my time at sea, or perhaps yachting or fishing; to care nothing for worldly power, and to be chronically unable to make money or even to keep what I have. Well – I suppose it is possible that I am gentle, kind and retiring, but when I suggested as much to a close friend he merely gave a bark of laughter and made some comments which I do not propose to reproduce here, if only because they would be of no interest to the reader. With regard to the sea, I admit to living within 500 yards of it, but I am no yachtsman; I paddle rather than swim, taking care to avoid treading upon sharp stones or slimy jellyfish; and I have never fished in my life, mainly because I would have a strong dislike of being yanked out of my natural habitat on the end of a bent pin, and I see no reason why any respectable fish should feel differently.

Astrologically, everything depends upon the positions of the planets against the starry background. There is a band stretching round the sky, known as the Zodiac, in which the Sun, Moon and principal planets are always to be found, because with one exception (Pluto) their paths are not sharply inclined to that of the Earth, and if you draw a plan of the Solar System upon a piece of flat paper you are not very far wrong. The Zodiac is divided into 12 constellations: Aries (the Ram), Taurus (the Bull), Gemini (the Twins), Cancer (the Crab), Leo (the Lion), Virgo (the Virgin), Libra (the Scales), Scorpio or Scorpius (the Scorpion), Sagittarius (the Archer), Capricornus (the Sea-goat), Aquarius (the Water-bearer) and Pisces (the Fishes). Belonging as I do to Pisces, I come officially at the tail-end of the procession, though as a matter of fact the astrological signs are now out of step with the actual constellations, because the direction of the Earth's axis wobbles slightly, and this alters the positions of both the poles and the equator of the sky. From a purely astronomical point of view Pisces is now the first constellation of the Zodiac, not the last.

To explain this more fully, I must say a little about astronomical terms. The Earth spins on its axis once a day, and the direction of the axis indicates the positions of the two celestial poles; the north pole is marked fairly closely by the bright star Polaris (there is no bright south polar star, the nearest naked-eye candidate being the obscure Sigma Octantis). And just as the terrestrial equator cuts the Earth in half, so the celestial equator cuts the sky in half, and we have a northern hemisphere and a southern hemisphere. As a matter of interest, the equator passes through the middle of the bright constellation of Orion, the Hunter.

Because the Earth completes one revolution round the Sun in one year (more accurately, in 365.25 days), the Sun itself seems to travel right round the sky in the same period. Its apparent path against the stars is known as the ecliptic, and because the Earth's axis is tilted to the perpendicular at an angle of 23½ degrees, the angle between the ecliptic and the celestial equator is also 23½ degrees. The points where the ecliptic and the equator cross are the equinoxes; the spring equinox or First Point of Aries when the Sun is travelling from south to north, and the Autumnal Equinox or First Point of Libra when the Sun is moving from north to south. In ancient times, the equinoxes really did lie in Aries and Libra respectively.

However, the Earth is not a perfect sphere. It bulges slightly at the equator (the equatorial diameter is 26 miles greater than the diameter as measured through the poles), and the Sun and Moon pull upon this bulge, causing the Earth to 'wobble' slightly in the manner of a gyroscope which is running down and has started to topple. The result is that the axis describes a small circle in the sky, over a period of about 26,000 years. Obviously this alters the positions on the celestial poles and hence, also, of the equinoxes. By now the First Point of Aries has shifted into the adjacent constellation, Pisces, while the First Point of Libra has moved into Virgo. This effect is known as precession, and explains why the astrological signs are now out of step with the constellations after which they are named – something which astrologers, as a class, prefer to forget.

Moreover, it is often forgotten that what we normally call a 'constellation' is not a true pattern at all. The stars are suns, and our Sun is nothing more than a run-of-the mill star; modern astronomers even relegate it to the status of a stellar dwarf. It is, on average, 93,000,000 miles away from us, but this is not much upon the astronomical scale, and all the other stars are far more remote, with distances which have to be measured in millions of millions of miles. For this reason, the mile is too short a unit of length to be convenient when we are discussing bodies beyond the Solar System, and a better unit is the light-year, which is a measure of length and not of time. Light moves at 186,000 miles per second, and yet it takes 4¼ years to reach us from the nearest star beyond the Sun; that is to say, this star (a dim red dwarf known as Proxima Centauri) is 4¼ light-years away. Sirius, the most brilliant star in the sky, is 8½ light-years away; Polaris lies at 680 light-years, and so on.

Now let us return to the constellations, and consider perhaps the most famous of them all – the Great Bear, known to astronomers as Ursa Major, to most Englishmen as the Plough, and to Americans as the Big Dipper. Its seven principal stars make up a pattern which cannot be misidentified, particularly since it is so far north in the sky that it never sets over the British Isles; you will always find it somewhere whenever the sky is sufficiently clear and dark. The two end stars in the Bear's tail are known as Mizar and Alkaid. (The names are Arabic; the official designations are Zeta and Eta Ursæ Majoris respectively.) Mizar is 78 light-years from us, while Alkaid is 210. Therefore the two stars are in no way associated, and merely happen to lie in much the same direction as seen from the Earth. In fact, Alkaid is much further away from Mizar than we are; and if we lay in the region between them, Mizar and Alkaid would be on opposite sides of the sky.

The same is true of other constellations, all of which are made up of entirely unassociated stars lying at very different distances. The patterns mean nothing at all, and in any case they are man-made. Nobody is quite sure who drew up the main constellation patterns which we now use; it may have been the Minoans of Ancient Crete, or the old Chaldæan shepherds who wanted to while away the long night hours. Extra groups have been added more recently; the sky contains such constellations as the Airpump, the Microscope and the Telescope, all of which would have looked rather out of place in classical times. (Other groups have been suggested. I particularly like Sceptrum Brandenburgicum, Officina Typographica and Honores Fredericii, but the International Astronomical Union put its foot firmly down 50 years ago, and reduced the accepted number of constellations to 88.)

Generally, the names of the constellations bear little resemblance to the forms of the objects they are meant to represent. For example, anyone who can make a sea-goat out of the pattern of Capricornus earns my undying admiration. And, of course, other early civilizations had constellations of their own; the Egyptians included a hawk and a hippopotamus. We happen to follow the Greek system, suitably modified, but this was due merely to chance.

Come, then, to my own constellation of Pisces, the Fishes. It is very faint, and consists entirely of various dim stars spread out at random. Why it should be regarded as 'watery' is not clear, and why it should be associated with kindness, gentleness and financial incompetence makes even less sense. Neither do I see why the brighter but equally formless group of Taurus, the Bull, should be masculine and brash.

Next, what of the planets? There are nine of them, all moving round the Sun at different distances: Mercury, Venus, the Earth, Mars, Jupiter, Saturn, Uranus, Neptune and Pluto. The last three were not known in ancient times, and were discovered in 1781, 1846 and 1930 respectively, though they seem to have had little difficulty in fitting in to the general astrological theme. It is quite likely that there may be one or two planets at still greater distances waiting to be found.

In astrology, a planet is said to be 'in' a constellation when it is seen against the background of stars making up that particular constellation. Thus in June 1982 Mars was 'in' Virgo. Yet Mars is close on the cosmical scale. It may come within 35,000,000 miles of us, which is negligible. To say that Mars is 'in' Virgo is about as logical as holding up your finger against a cloudy sky and claiming that your finger is 'in' the clouds.

These, then, are the facts. The positions of the Sun, Moon and planets at the time of birth are all-important astrologically, and so are the subsequent movements; thus if Saturn and Mars seem close together it may mean that disaster lies ahead, so that there is no chance whatsoever of a happy meeting with a dark lady coming over the water. A year or two ago I cast my horoscope, and found that according to all the omens I ought to have a major success at some physical activity. I was playing cricket that day, and so far as I can remember my bowling analysis was 0 for 87. Clearly there had been a slight error somewhere or other.

In short: the planets are essentially local, the stars are very remote indeed, and the constellation patterns have no real significance. Neither, therefore, have the astrological signs, which are in any case out of step. It is also true that an extra constellation (Ophiuchus, the Serpent-bearer) intrudes into the Zodiac between Scorpius and Sagittarius, but has not been given a sign of its own, because all the vacant places have been taken and the hapless Serpent-bearer has been left out on a limb.

Astrology goes back a long way, to the time when the Earth was regarded as the most important of all bodies, and to lie in the centre of the universe. Most astronomers of olden days were also astrologers, and up to the time of Isaac Newton – that is to say, the late-seventeenth century, astrology was still regarded as a true science. Ancient rulers and generals placed great faith in astrologers, and at least one major war was swung upon astrological advice. This was the Peloponnesian War, fought between the Greek city-states of Athens and Sparta. I do not want to delve into history, but it is worth recording that when the Athenians had invaded the island of Sicily, and were in danger of annihilation, their commander, Nicias, delayed evacuation because of an eclipse of the Moon which, said the astrologers, meant that he had better stay where he was. He did; and he never had another chance to escape. That, in the long run, was the end of Athens as a great power.

Astrology still lingers on in two guises: that of the 'What the Stars Foretell' newspaper columnists, and the serious practitioners who are in deadly earnest, casting horoscopes and handing themselves impressive degrees such as D. F. Astrol. S. It is common in India, and it was widely reported that one Prime Minister, Mrs Indira Gandhi, timed the 1971 election on astrological advice – I admit, winning it handsomely – while as recently as January 1982 the date of the marriage of Princess Chulabhorn, daughter of King Bhumibol of Thailand, was fixed at a moment which the Court astrologers regarded as propitious. It also has a foothold in the United States and in Europe. There have been famous supporters of it, notably the eccentric educationalist Rudolf Steiner (who also considered the Earth to be flat) and even Hitler, who apparently believed the astrologers who assured him that the Western Powers would not dare to go to war in 1939.

It seems that the psychiatrists and psychologists are largely responsible for this, because many of them take astrology seriously even today. C. G. Jung was one typical example. There has recently been qualified support from H. J. Eysenck and his colleague D. K. B. Nias, who have issued a book in which they give some credence to the work of a French husband-and-wife team, the Gauquelins, about whom it is worth saying a little more.

Basically, the Gauquelins have been tabulating the positions of the planets at the times of birth and death of people in certain definite walks of life. Since the Earth is spinning round, each planet appears to rise and set once every 24 hours (though, of course, this often happens in daylight). The planets rise in an easterly direction, reach their highest point at the moment of culmination – termed by the astrologers 'midheaven' – and set towards the west. The

Gauquelins divided the apparent path of each planet across the sky into 12 sectors, and concluded that the risings and settings of the planets were of real significance. Thus, if a baby happened to be born when Mars or Saturn was rising, he (or she) was quite likely to become a doctor. Mars was linked with sportsmen – and after all, Mars himself was the virile God of War. . . .

Of course, things were not *quite* right. In particular, the Sun and Moon seemed to have no effect at all. Neither did Mercury, or the three outer planets Uranus, Neptune and Pluto. Of the ten Solar System bodies studied by most astrologers, the Gauquelins therefore promptly threw out six, because they did not fit. It then became painfully clear that with ordinary people even the effects of the four remaining bodies (Venus, Mars, Jupiter and Saturn) did not fit either. The choice of personalities had to be narrowed down, and at length, after casting aside more than half the bodies of the Solar System and selecting suitable groups of people, they decided that they had reached some results which were really significant.

Let it be said at once that there is no doubt about the sincerity of the Gauquelins, or those psychiatrists who have investigated their findings. Thousands of tests have been carried out. But it is hard to see how the results can be taken seriously, because if you juggle with figures for long enough it would indeed be odd if no apparent relationships could be found. Given enough patience, it is possible to prove practically anything. Not long ago I was giving a lecture in London to an audience composed of people from all walks of life, and I decided to carry out an astrological test of my own. The audience nobly filled in the questionnaires that I distributed. Upon analysing the results, I found that a significant percentage of those born under the sign of Leo disliked beetroot, while Aquarius appeared to be linked with tennis players, and male members of the audience who had been born under Aries tended to have Christian names beginning with the letters C, R or T.

Before leaving the Gauquelins, I wonder what they would conclude from the horoscope of a baby born in North Norway during the spring of 1982, when all four planets involved were so far south of the celestial equator that as seen from that part of the world they never rose at all? Presumably the luckless infant would be deprived of all the advantages of astrological influences!

You cannot but admire the astrologers' techniques. Most of their predictions are so tightly wrapped in cotton wool that they can be interpreted in almost any way, and when asked just why the positions of the planets can affect human destiny they admit, with refreshing candour, that they don't know. It has something to do with Vibrations, but that is as much as they can say.

I apologize for this somewhat lengthy digression, but I felt it necessary because throughout the ages the astrologers have been vocal in predicting that the end is nigh. What alarmed them most (and still does) is a gathering of planets in any one particular part of the heavens. Of course, we are again dealing with line of sight effects; if, for instance, Venus and Jupiter happen to lie side by side, we must not jump to the conclusion that they are genuinely close together. On average, Venus is 67,000,000 miles from the Sun, while for Jupiter the distance is 483,000,000 miles, so that the two planets must always be hundreds of millions of miles apart. Appearances can be deceptive.

The planets move round the Sun not only at different distances, but also in widely differing periods, ranging from 88 days in the case of Mercury up to almost 248 years for Pluto. Inevitably, then, there are times when they enter the same part of the Zodiac. There was a major conjunction of several planets in the year 1186, and this was quite enough for the astrologers to forecast all sorts of dire events which, however, failed to materialize. Yet the climax was reached in 1524, and now we come, at last, to Johann Stöffler.

Stöffler was born in Lustingen, in Suebia, in 1452. He was certainly no dunce, and he made his way to the University of Tübingen, where he soon became well known. He wrote various books, mainly on astrology, as well as an excellent treatise on the ancient astronomical measuring instrument known as the astrolabe; he was also concerned with calendar reform. His fame spread, and he was regarded as a very wise man indeed. One story about him (possibly apochryphal, though I would like to believe it!) relates how the stars told him that on a certain day he would be in grave danger from a falling body. Prudently he stayed indoors, but made the elementary mistake of reaching for a book which lay on a high shelf; the book made an unceremonious descent, and landed upon his head, which did not please him in the least even though he had proved his point.

During his routine calculations, Stöffler suddenly made a dramatic discovery. In February 1524 the planets Mars, Jupiter and Saturn would all be in Pisces. Of course, Pisces is a watery sign;

The Leonid meteor shower of 1833, when it was said that meteors 'rained down like snowflakes' – regarded by William Miller as a sign of approaching doom.

ABOVE: The great comet of 1843 with its brilliant tail stretching across the sky, causing considerable alarm and despondency, particularly among the Millerites!
BELOW: An astrological chart; it is by this sort of diagram that astrologers claim to be able to give reliable information about a person's character and destiny(!)

Mars and Saturn are generally of evil influence – and the only logical result would be a great flood, which would destroy civilization and might even cause the end of the world itself. Nothing could be more straightforward.

Stöffler felt it his duty to issue a general warning, and accordingly he did so. Other astrologers agreed with him and, as 1524 approached there was evidence of panic. Almanacs sprang up like mushrooms, all bearing the same message, and the alarm was not confined to Germany. It spread over much of Europe – not, so far as I can tell, to England – and even penetrated to parts of Asia and Africa; Stöffler's reputation was so great that nobody felt inclined to doubt him. According to contemporary reports, the terror far surpassed that inspired by the Millerites long afterwards. Moreover, many Top People joined in.

What was to be done? If water were to be the main agent of destruction, the obvious remedy was to build boats, and this is precisely what many people did. In France, President Auriol of the University of Toulouse set to work building what was to all intents and purposes a Noah-type ark. Not that he meant to collect any animals; he wanted the ark for himself and his nearest and dearest, but an ark it was, none the less. All over Europe, trade and commerce came to a grinding halt. The essential thing was to build boats, boats and still more boats, so that before long the Rhine was more crowded than the Serpentine on a sunny summer's day. Fields were left uncultivated, and most of the ordinary routine of life was in abeyance. Some people decided to drink themselves to death rather than face the coming holocaust, while others adopted pious attitudes and resolved to make the best of it. There were cases of men and women who sold all their possessions in order to finance their boat-building, while others made haste to the tops of mountains, presumably hoping that the peaks would poke out above the raging waters.

Royalty was not unaffected. The Emperor Charles V of Spain sent out his wise men to look for safe places, assuming that the floods would not be total and that some parts of the world would escape being drowned – if, of course, the world survived at all. Another story, perhaps again apocryphal, relates how a German count named von Iggleheim was attacked by a fear-crazed mob when he refused to share his boat with the common people, and was fatally injured. As 20 February approached, the day given by

Stöffler, the panic reached its height. Nothing like it had been seen in Europe before, and probably nothing like it will be seen again.

Ironically, most of February was dry and warm, but on the 21st rain began, and continued steadily until everything was wet and soggy. Still, this was very different from a major flood, and as March came the general panic started to abate. Could there have been an error? One man who thought so was Johann Carion, astrologer to the Emperor Joachim I of Brandenburg. Stöffler, said Carion, was wrong. The date of the disaster was not 20 February, but 15 July of the following year, 1525. By then things had more or less reverted to normal over most of the mainland, but the Elector prudently decided that he had better take action.

Once again I depend upon contemporary reports which may or may not be reliable. If they are, then the afternoon of 15 July witnessed a strange scene. As the clouds gathered, the gates of the Castle of Berlin-Köln were flung open, and the State coach came out, carrying the Elector and his family; behind it were other vehicles, containing all the most treasured family possessions which were even remotely portable. The procession made its way to the top of a nearby hill, where it stayed until nightfall. The only celestial manifestation was a shower, and eventually the Elector decided to go home, leaving Carion behind in disgrace. Just as the coach arrived back at the Castle gates, a flash of lightning struck it and killed all four horses. The Elector immediately recalled Carion, though what happened later is not on record.

Slowly the last traces of the panic died away, but there were echoes of it for some time. President Auriol dismantled his ark, and when questioned about it said rather lamely that he had merely wanted it for a fishing trip. Stöffler himself was not in the least abashed, and produced another prediction, this time for 1588: 'If in this terrible year the globe is not dissolved in dust, and the land and sea be not destroyed, every kingdom will be overthrown and humanity will suffer pain.' By that time Stöffler would have reached the ripe old age of 148, so presumably he felt justified in taking a chance. He actually died in 1531, and nothing happened in 1588 apart, of course, from the Spanish Armada, which had no astrological connections whatever. Note, however, that this time Stöffler was not relying upon any planetary conjunction. He selected that particular date because it was the eighth year following the 1,580th anniversary of the birth of Christ.

Another astrologer, one Cyprian Leöwitz, drew attention to a conjunction due in 1584 – not so imposing as Stöffler's, but still marked enough to be alarming. According to a contemporary writer named Louis Guyon, 'the terror of the populace was extreme, and the churches could not hold the multitudes which fled to them for refuge; many made their wills without stopping to think that this would avail them little if the world were really to perish, while others donated goods to the clergy, in the hope that their prayers would postpone the Day of Judgement'.

Before passing on, let us pause to dispose of two characters who were not specifically concerned with astrology, but who nevertheless claimed to be able to see into the future. One was Mother Shipton, who is believed to have lived from 1488 to 1562, in which case she was Stöffler's contemporary. There is little doubt that Mother Shipton really existed, though she is so deeply woven into legend that it is impossible to separate truth from myth, and she seems to have been the prototype of those witches so roughly treated by Sir Rupert Murgatroyd in *Ruddigore*. ('Sir Rupert Murgatroyd, his leisure and his riches He ruthlessly employed in persecuting witches.') Apparently, she predicted the Fire of London, and one verse attributed to her reads:

> Houses shall appear in the vales below,
> And covered by hail and snow;
> The world then to an end shall come
> In nineteen hundred and ninety-one.

The other seer was Nostradamus, whose fame is still great even today. He was French, and lived from 1503 to 1566. He specialized in rhyming prophecies, and several times he hit the nail squarely on the head. (Coincidence? Probably. As was once said, 'it is impossible always to be wrong', unless of course you happen to be a psychiatrist.) Among Nostradamus' *Centuries* we find:

> *Quand Georges Dieu crucifiera,*
> *Que Marc le ressuscitera,*
> *Et que St Jean le portera,*
> *La fin du monde arrivera.*

To translate: when Easter falls on 25 April (St Mark's Day), Holy Friday will be on 23 April (St George's Day) and Corpus Christi on 24 June (St John's Day), and the world will end. It was Camille

Flammarion, the celebrated French astronomer, who pointed out that there is something odd about this. The calendar was not reformed until 1582, when it was officially changed from the old Julian into the modern Gregorian. Before that, Easter could not possibly fall on 25 April, and yet Nostradamus died in 1566. Since then, Easter has fallen on 25 April (its last possible date) in 1666, 1734, 1886 and 1943. The next occasion will be in 2038. Let us hope that Nostradamus was wrong.

Another verse (*Century* One, section or quatrain 48) gives a rather different story:

> *Vingt ans du règne de la lune passez,*
> *Sept mil ans autre tiendra sa monarche;*
> *Quand le Soleil prendra ses jours lassez,*
> *Lors accomplit et mine ma prophetie,*

or 'When twenty years of the Moon's reign have passed, another will take up his reign for 7,000 years. When the exhausted Sun takes up his cycle, then my prophecy and my threats will be accomplished.' If Nostradamus believed that he was writing at the start of a new 'cycle of the Moon', there is a link with an old Middle Ages theory that the world will come to an end at the beginning of the seventh millennium, an idea coming originally from the Book of Enoch, which was removed by the Church from the Canon in AD 300. Nostradamus also has a relevant passage in *Century* Ten, quatrain 74, the translation of which is: 'The year of the great seventh number accomplished, it will appear at the time of the games of slaughter, not far from the age of the great millennium, when the dead will come out of their graves.'

Candidly I am not particularly impressed with Nostradamus, who was at best obscure, and will do no more than mention the eclipse of 12 August 1654, interpreted as being decidedly menacing, though for no obvious reason. When the world failed to end, one clergyman preached a sermon in which he said that God had relented, and had given humanity a fortnight's grace, so that he had postponed not only the Last Trump but also the eclipse itself. (So let us skip several hundred years and come to our own age, with Professor Porta's 'League of Planets' and, in particular, Dr John Gribbin's 'Jupiter Effect'.

Chapter Three
The Jupiter Effect

Astrologers depend for their forecasts on the positions of the planets against the starry background. Their end-of-the-world predictions have been based upon mysticism and occultism, to say nothing of those elusive 'vibrations'. However, there have been other scares connected with the planets, not for their astrological powers, but for their purely physical effects. And first in the field seems to have been Professor Alberto Porta.

Porta was an oddity. I have never been able to find out whether he was really entitled to be called a professor; I have a nasty suspicion that he wasn't, though I may be doing him an injustice. He was Italian-born, but emigrated to the United States at some time during the 1870s, and studied seismology and meteorology. He did have some success in predicting earthquakes, though again it was probably sheer luck (even today we cannot tell just when or where earthquakes will strike, though we know a great deal more about them than we did a few decades ago). Porta published weather forecasts in San Francisco, where there was a small newspaper printed in Italian for the benefit of immigrants, and in 1917 he gave his opinion that there would be a violent shock along the Pacific coast on either 27 or 28 December. On the 25th, a serious tremor ruined Guatemala City, and further jolts occurred on the following days, so that Porta's warnings came to be taken quite seriously by the general public.

He then turned his attention to the planets and found, quite correctly, that in December 1919 most of them would be roughly lined up. Mercury, Venus, Mars, Jupiter, Saturn and Neptune were on one side of the Sun, and Uranus on the other side, so that all of them were pulling gravitationally in the same sense. Porta called it the 'League of Planets', and drew dire conclusions from it.

According to his theory, sunspots, the dark patches on the solar disk, were produced by the electromagnetic pulls of the planets. Actually, we now know – or think we know – that the planets have nothing whatsoever to do with sunspots; there is a semi-regular cycle of 11 years, when sunspots are particularly numerous, so that the Sun was very active in 1958, 1969 and 1980, and will be so again in 1991. The spots are centres of strong magnetic fields, and violent outbursts known as flares, associated with them, emit streams of charged particles which enter our upper air and interfere with wireless reception, as well as producing auroræ or polar lights and causing the compass needle to fluctuate. However, the origin of all these phenomena lies in the Sun itself, not outside. Porta's ideas were very different. I quote:

'Owing to the strange grouping of six mighty planets such as has not been seen for a score of centuries, the United States will next December be swept by the most terrific weather cataclysm since human history began. It will be caused by the largest sunspot on record. It will appear on 17 December 1919, as a vast wound in the side of the Sun – a gigantic explosion of flaming gases, leaping hundreds of thousands of miles out into space. It will be rich enough in electromagnetic waves to fling the atmosphere of our planet into a disturbance without precedent or parallel. There will be hurricanes, lightning, colossal rains. There will also be gigantic lava eruptions, great earthquakes, to say nothing of floods and fearful cold . . . Six planets will be massed in the narrow limit of 26 degrees on the same side of the Sun. Directly opposite, coming into opposition with this gigantic League of Planets, will be the huge planet Uranus. The magnetic currents between Uranus and the six planets will pierce the Sun like a mighty spear. Be warned in advance. Tremendous events will happen from 17 to 20 December 1919, and afterwards!'

In view of his previous successes, Porta's words caused some panic, though it could not be compared even remotely with those caused by Stöffler or Miller. The Nautical Almanac Office of the United States Naval Observatory was bombarded by anxious enquirers, and was forced to issue a disclaimer, but people kept a wary eye on the Sun, and it is related that some miners in Oklahoma refused to go underground in case they would be trapped. (This is surely an original reason for a strike!) In fact no exceptional sunspots appeared, and there were no earthquakes. I may add that the largest sunspot on record, that of April 1947, did not coincide with any planetary conjunctions.

I may be accused of cheating here, because up to now I have been discussing the actual end of the world, and this was not what Porta predicted; all he said was that his 'League of Planets' would produce serious disturbances, which is not the same thing. After the usual and inevitable anti-climax, he went back to forecasting gales and minor earthquakes. I have been unable to find out what eventually happened to him. He had had his moment of notoriety, and he subsided gently into the background.

·An interesting planetary conjunction in 1962 passed off without much comment, though astrologers in India were somewhat alarmed by it. So we come now to very recent times, and the work of two British science writers, Dr John Gribbin of Sussex University and his colleague Mr Stephen Plagemann. Let it be said at once that they come into a different category from Alberto Porta. First, they have perfectly valid degrees in astronomy; secondly, their forecasts depend upon gravitational forces rather than electromagnetic ones. Yet in a way they have come back to what may be termed a 'League of Planets', and their book, *The Jupiter Effect*, first published in 1974 and since reissued several times, created a tremendous amount of interest, mixed with alarm.

The main theme of the book was that during 1982 all the main planets would line up, in a 'superconjunction' which would cause dire effects upon the Earth. Jupiter, the most massive of the planets, would have the main triggering effect – hence the title of the book. But before going on, it seems only right to say something about the overall pattern of the Solar System itself.

Of course the controlling body is our own star, the Sun, which is a huge globe approximately 865,000 miles in diameter and with a mass almost 330,000 times that of the Earth. (You could pack a million bodies the volume of the Earth inside the Sun and still leave plenty of room to spare.) The surface temperature is almost 6,000 degrees Centigrade, and the temperature at the core reaches the incredible value of at least 14,000,000 degrees. It is radiating not because it is burning, but because of nuclear reactions taking place inside it, a point to which I will return later. Even mighty Jupiter has less than one-thousandth the mass of the Sun.

The Solar System is divided neatly into two parts. The inner region contains four comparatively small, solid planets: Mercury,

Venus, the Earth and Mars, with mean distances from the Sun ranging between 36,000,000 miles for Mercury out to 141,500,000 miles for Mars. Beyond Mars there is a wide gap, in which move thousands of worlds known as the asteroids or minor planets. Beyond this again come the giants: Jupiter, Saturn, Uranus and Neptune, all of which are much larger than the Earth and are of completely different make-up, with solid cores, mainly liquid interiors and outer layers of gas. Finally there is the strange little world Pluto, which seems to be in a class of its own and may not be worthy of true planetary status.

Because the revolution periods are so different, it is only natural that there must be times when the planets move into an approximate line. In their original book, Gribbin and Plagemann stated that between 1977 and 1982 the planets of the Solar System would move into an unusual alignment in which every planet would be in conjunction with every other planet, so that all the planets would be aligned on the same side of the Sun. Such an alignment occurs only once in 179 years. They went on to predict a depressing sequence of events:

1. The combined gravitational pulls of the planets would stretch out the Sun.

2. This tidal stretching would cause great disturbances on the solar surface, increasing the numbers of sunspots and solar activity in general.

3. The active areas on the Sun would shoot out electrified particles, many of which would shower on to the Earth.

4. Consequently, the Earth's rate of rotation would be altered, either by the effects of the charged particles on our own magnetic field, or by interactions with the Earth's atmosphere, thereby altering the overall atmospheric circulation and increasing the friction between the air and the solid ground.

5. This change in rotation, even though very small, would cause strains in the Earth's globe, triggering off earthquakes along lines of weakness in the crust.

In particular they mentioned the San Francisco area, where a weak line in the Earth's crust known as the San Andreas Fault has long been viewed with misgivings. There was a major quake in 1906, which devastated the city, and there will almost certainly be another in the foreseeable future.

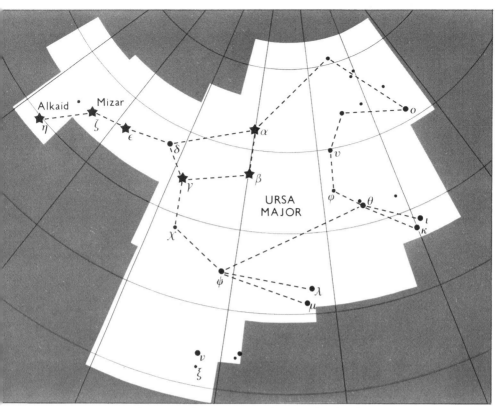

ABOVE: The Great Bear with its seven famous stars making up the Plough or Dipper pattern; Mizar, with its small companion Alcor, is much closer to us than Alkaid.
BELOW: Fishing – from an ark. Whether President Auriol actually landed any fish or whether his amazing ark was ever used for this innocent purpose, is not on record!

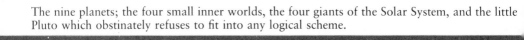

Mercury

Venus

Earth

Uranus

Saturn

Jupiter

Pluto

Neptune

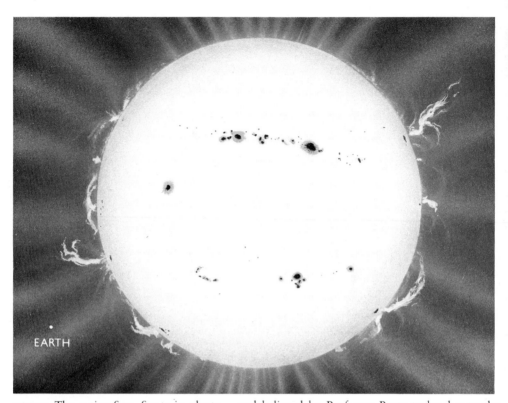

EARTH

ABOVE: The active Sun. Spots in plenty – and believed by Professor Porta to be due to the gravitational pulls of the planets upon the Sun's fiercely hot surface.
BELOW: Relative positions of the planets for 1982, the year when, according to The *Jupiter Effect*-writers, they should have been lined up.

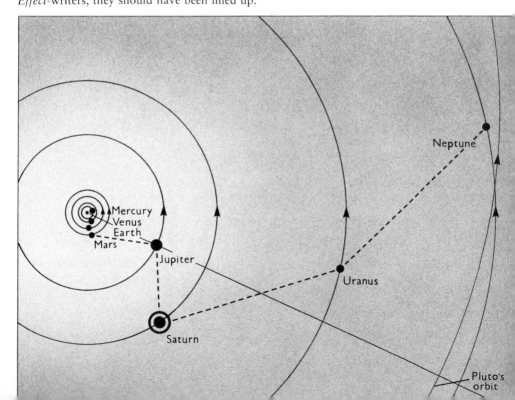

Mercury
Venus
Earth
Mars
Jupiter
Saturn
Uranus
Neptune
Pluto's orbit

All this sounds plausible enough, but there are two immediate objections. One is that no planetary alignment was due between 1977 and 1982, as any rough calculation would show. In 1982, the Gribbin 'critical year', it was quite true that the planets were in the same quadrant of the Solar System, but there was not even an approximate lining-up. Look, for instance, at the situation in March 1982. The angular distance between two of the giants, Saturn and Neptune, was not far short of a right angle!

The second fatal objection could be demonstrated by simple subtraction. According to Gribbin and Plagemann, the 'alignment' occurs every 179 years. Take 179 away from 1982; we have 1803, and there was no major earthquake anywhere near that date; we have to go back to 1783 (in the Calabria area of Italy) or forwards to 1811 (a series of shocks in New Madrid, in the United States).

It has been calculated that the tidal stretching of the Sun could never amount to more than a few millimetres at most, which is not much when considering a globe 865,000 miles in diameter. Moreover, we now know that the solar surface pulsates up and down to the extent of about six miles in periods ranging from several minutes to several hours, which is more than enough to mask any planetary effects completely. (Remember, the Sun contains 99.86 per cent of the entire mass of the Solar System.) Another way of putting it is that the maximum planetary tides on the Sun are about 2,700,000 times smaller than the Moon's tidal effects upon the Earth.

It is also interesting to work out the tidal pulls on the Sun caused by each planet, taking the Earth's pull as unity. The figures are as follows:

Mercury (maximum)	1.89
Venus	0.54
Earth	1
Mars (maximum)	0.041
Jupiter	2.26
Saturn	0.11
Uranus	0.002
Neptune	0.0006
Pluto	0.00000008

Therefore we can promptly forget all about Mars and the four outer planets, which even when combined have negligible pulls compared with that of Jupiter. The idea that they could produce any measurable effects is not valid. Gribbin also forecast that the 'alignment' would delay the time of sunspot maximum until 1982. It didn't.

Nevertheless, a scare had been started, and a programme at the London Planetarium, entitled 'Omens', did not help the situation in the least, because it treated the theory seriously. I did persuade the Planetarium officials to take it off, but not before I had begun to receive letters from parents whose children had been badly frightened, and as 1982 approached many official bodies – including the Kitt Peak National Observatory in America, and the Royal Greenwich Observatory in England – were forced to issue denials. Even in my own case I must have received at least 500 letters about it, and though I presented a special *Sky at Night* programme on BBC television the letters continued to pour in.

By now the scare had spread beyond Europe and the United States. There were minor panics in India, where people turned to astrologers for advice; a guru called B. V. Raman reassured them by saying that only Los Angeles would be destroyed, not the whole world. On the critical day, 10 March, the New Delhi *Herald* forecast that the planetary alignment would cause disease, riots, labour unrest and, of course, an earthquake, while 'a strange epidemic affecting the abdomen' would stalk India. The Brahmin priests in Calcutta performed special ceremonies, which involved the kindling of small fires and paying tribute to the fire-god Agni. Over in Pekin (or, to give it its modern name, Beijing) the *Youth Daily* reissued a statement from the Chinese Government to the effect that any fears about the approaching end of the world were groundless.

Things were no better in the United States. One astronomer at Kitt Peak received an agitated call from an elderly woman: her grandson had his ninth birthday on 10 March – would he survive to see it? On the day itself came a programme transmitted from many local radio stations featuring one Boyd Quate, a long-range weather forecaster. The programme had been compiled by the News Information Weekly Service (NIWS) and was compèred by Harold Joffe from Portsmouth, Virginia.

Following a general introduction, Joffe stated that sunspots and magnetic outbreaks on the solar surface 'have everything to do with our weather, and they are under the influence of the "Jupiter

Effect"'. After a contribution from Quate, to the effect that something in outer space was disturbing his magnetic data (whatever they might have been), Joffe turned to the exceptionally cold winter over North America, which again he attributed to the unusual planetary alignment. He went on: 'Scientific correlations between the "Jupiter Effect" and the weather are sketchy, but they occur none the less,' and Quate agreed that 'it does happen'. Perhaps fittingly, the programme ended with a contribution from an astrologer, Carole Devine, who was quite sure that 'there is no area of living which is not being affected' by the alignment, and that 'the U.S. chart will be under a lot of stress this year. If there is going to be a war, it would be inclined to start during this time.'

All in all it was a remarkable episode, and it demonstrates that even in the Space Age any wild rumour is liable to spread once it has been sparked off.

(In a further article, Dr Gribbin has described planetary alignments and ancient Chinese ideas about them which indicate that there may be effects on our climate, with even a new Ice Age on the way. Fortunately I don't think this will happen either! There is no conceivable reason why it should!)

Yet though the Jupiter Effect is non-existent, the arrangement of the major planets in a gentle curve near the end of the 1970s proved to be a boon to the spacecraft planners. Mars, Venus and Mercury can be reached in a few months, but the outer members of the Sun's family are much further away. Jupiter is reasonably accessible, in less than two years, but then there is a vast gap before we reach the orbit of Saturn, and Uranus and Neptune are more remote still. You tend to forget how spread out the giant planets really are, and an ordinary map of the Solar System can be misleading, just as an average European may look at a chart of the southern hemisphere and think that it is almost possible to stand on the Queensland coast of Australia and hop across to New Zealand. If a spacecraft is destined to go to Uranus, for instance, then the orbit of Saturn is less than half-way.

The favoured method is to use the technique which I have rather irreverently called interplanetary snooker. It involves using the gravitational pull of one planet to send the spacecraft hurtling out towards another. Thus Voyager 2, launched in 1977, by-passed Jupiter in 1979; it was swung round the giant planet towards a rendezvous with Saturn, which was duly accomplished in 1981.

Saturn's pull was then used to send Voyager out to Uranus, which is due to be encountered in January 1986, after which Uranus will dispatch it out to its final target, Neptune, in August 1989. The principle has been tested, and it works well. Without it, journeys to Saturn and beyond would take a very long time indeed, and this will be the case in the future, because it will not be for many decades that the four large planets will once more be suitably placed. If all goes well, all our neighbour worlds, except one, will have been studied from close range within the next decade. Pluto alone has been perforce neglected, but it is in any case a very junior member of the Sun's family; it is smaller than our Moon, and both it and its satellite, Charon, are probably made up largely of ice.

Finally, mention must be made of Monsieur Louis Jacot, whose theories were published in 1977 in a book entitled *Earth's Flight Beyond* (beyond what, I am frankly unsure). Monsieur Jacot believes that space is filled with a substance called ether, and that the Sun throws out planets now and then, after which these planets move outwards in spiral paths. There is a kind of general post, with Mercury moving out to the orbit of Venus, Venus to that of the Earth, and so on. As the distances increase, the density of the surrounding ether falls away; the planets expand, and eventually go off 'pop'. This he takes to be the ultimate fate of the Earth, though not, I am glad to say, for a long time yet.

Monsieur Jacot's warnings, given in deep sincerity, have not really impressed the scientific world. In fact it may be said that they have caused all the impact of a feather falling on to damp blotting-paper, and they are not likely to cause anything in the way of alarm. But they are intriguing none the less, and I, for one, read them with marked, albeit rather stunned, fascination.

I am afraid that this has been a rather discursive chapter, but it has had to cover quite a number of ideas, some of them less logical than others. Astrology, that weird relic of the past, hangs on grimly, but we can certainly discount both Professor Porta's electromagnetic forces as agents of destruction, and neither need we fear the combined gravitational pulls of the planets. I suppose that the approaching end of the 20th century will be hailed by a few seers as significant, and at least some people will sit up on the night of 31 December 1999 to make sure that we are still here at the dawn of 1 January 2000 (many of them forgetting that the first day of the new century will be 1 January not of 2000, but of 2001). All the same, there is unlikely to be as much apprehension as there was 1,000 years ago.

What, then, of the planets themselves? I need only say that they move in completely stable paths, and the notion that any of them will 'run wild' and crash into us will make any mathematician smile pityingly. I will return to this theme later, when discussing Dr Velikovsky, but I can assure you that there is no need for any misgivings. Yet it was Saturn which produced a curious if minor scare in the little town of Dinkelsbühl, 40 miles from Nürnberg, as recently as 1946. For some reason which I have been utterly unable to discover, the rumour went round that Saturn had fallen out of its orbit, and was racing towards us in the manner of a homing pigeon. The Allied authorities, at that time firmly in charge of Germany, found that there was marked reluctance on the part of the local inhabitants to leave their homes in order to go to work, and efforts were made to track down the source of the rumour. I do not think that it was ever unravelled, and before long the fears died away. Presumably muttering things such as 'Donner und blitzen!' 'Damit!' and 'Besonders', everyone went back to work.

Saturn is still intact. So is Dinkelsbühl. And so are we.

Chapter Four

The Menacing Moon

O Moon, lovely Moon with the beautiful face,
Careering throughout the bound'ries of space,
Whenever I see you, I think in my mind
Shall I ever, O ever, behold thy behind?

I first came across this rhyme many years ago, when, at the age of about nine, I started to take more than a passing interest in the Moon. From all accounts it was written by a housemaid in the service of a well-known poet, who had done her best to combine verse with sheer science. Actually there was more than a grain of truth in the rhyme, because the Moon does keep the same face turned permanently towards us, and from the Earth there is 41 per cent of the lunar surface which we can never see. Until 1959, when the Russians dispatched their camera-carrying vehicle, Luna 3, on a round trip and managed to obtain photographs of the hidden regions, the 'other side of the Moon' was completely unknown. Today, of course, there are 27 men who have seen it – the crews of Apollos 8, and 10 to 17 inclusive – and we know that it is just as barren and just as crater-scarred as the hemisphere we can see on any clear night when the Moon is well placed.

Why does the Moon behave in this curious way? The answer may be summed up in two words: 'tidal friction', and it is this tidal friction which has led some people to suggest that the Moon will eventually destroy the Earth, or at least all life on it. As I am particularly fond of the Moon, I must say at the outset that this will not happen; but before going into any more detail, let me discuss another theory which once had a considerable following, and which was linked, in a way, with the end of the world.

It originated with an Austrian engineer named Hans Hörbiger. I never met him (he died before the war), but I have known people who did, and it is generally agreed that he was an odd character. He published his major work, *Glazial-Kosmogenie*, in 1913, and expected it to become a sort of scientific bible. It ran to nearly 800 pages, and was, I gather, written in an exaggerated Teutonic style, combining heaviness with dogmatism. Anyone who disagreed with it was automatically classed as an enemy, and Herr Hörbiger was firmly convinced that he was being persecuted by orthodox scientists who had no wish to see their cherished ideas swept away. His book led on to what was called WEL, an abbreviation for Welt Eis Lehre, or Cosmic Ice Theory, because ice was the key to the whole situation.

According to Hörbiger, and to his disciple H. S. Bellamy, practically everything in the universe, apart from the Earth and the Sun, is made up of ice. The stars are ice-blocks, and so they are freezing cold instead of boiling hot. The planet Mars has an icy coating 250 miles deep, and the Martian canals are simply cracks in the surface (it was not until much later that the canals were, alas, found to be due to nothing more than tricks of the eye). The Moon is equally icy, and the same is true of all the other members of the Solar System, so that the universe is a distinctly chilly place.

Next we come to space itself, which, according to Hörbiger and Bellamy, is filled with rarefied hydrogen. Now any gas, however thin, will set up a certain amount of resistance to any object ploughing through it, and Hörbiger claimed that this resistance would slow a planet down. The effect would admittedly be slight, but over the centuries it would mount up. Therefore, each planet will spiral steadily down towards the Sun, as will the minor members of the Solar System such as asteroids and meteoroids. When one of these ice-blocks falls into the Sun, it produces a sunspot before being unceremoniously snuffed out.

This will also be the fate of the Earth. Eventually, as the steady drag caused by the hydrogen begins to overcome our orbital motion, the world will approach the Sun, and even before it is vapourized it will drop on to the solar surface, producing a particularly large sunspot. To the disciples of WEL, this is a fate which cannot be avoided, though they did admit that it is not imminent, mainly because the Earth is unique in being devoid of an icy shell.

However, a more pressing danger comes from the Moon, which also is being braked by the hydrogen, and is spiralling down towards us. It is not the first Moon. In previous times the Earth has accumulated at least six others, all of which have been composed of ice, and all of which have been torn apart by the strong pull of gravity as they have swung dangerously close. Each time an ice-moon is disrupted there are violent cataclysms, one of which (of course!) resulted in the drowning of the lost continent of Atlantis, while an earlier one altered conditions here so greatly that the dinosaurs, then lords of the world, simply curled up their toes and died. The last ex-moon broke up in biblical times – and need I add that this was the cause of Noah's flood?

Bellamy (who took over where Hörbiger left off) calculated that our present Moon was captured by the Earth about 13,000 years ago, and is now drawing steadily closer and closer. Finally it will come within what is known as the Roche limit, and disaster will follow. This limit, named after the last-century French mathematician Édouard Roche, who was the first to describe it, may be called the danger zone round the Earth, where the gravitational pull is so strong that any fragile body will be disrupted (this does not apply to a structure such as a space station, which is of rigid construction). The Roche limit lies about 5,700 miles above the ground, so that our present Moon is well beyond it.

However, again citing Bellamy, the hydrogen braking will go remorselessly on. The Moon will come nearer and nearer until it looms in the sky as a large, terrifying body, causing tremendous tides which will flood most of the continents. Then the earthquakes will start; the lands will twist and writhe as though in agony, and the tilt of the axis will be altered, so that the climates will change too. We may imagine polar bears striding through the present-day Sahara, while rhinoceroses and hippopotami will make for the sunnier climes of Greenland or Antarctica. Men will face a crisis, and not many of the human race will survive. Will this be the end? Not really – at least, Bellamy didn't think so. When the Moon comes within the Roche limit it will shatter into frozen fragments, and these will rain down on the Earth, so that going for an afternoon walk will involve the serious risk of being hit on the head by a tumbling ice-block. At last the supply of fragments will be exhausted; the Earth will 'snap back' into its previous state, and a new era will begin, to last until we capture another ice-moon and the story is repeated. The end will come with the arrival of a more massive moon, which will shatter the world into tiny pieces.

ABOVE: Break-up of an ice-moon, raining its fragments down upon the Earth with devastating results, according to Hörbiger and the disciples of WEL.
BELOW: How the Moon moves. It may hide the Sun and eclipse it; it may also pass into the Earth's shadow and be hidden for a while or at least, turned dim and coppery.

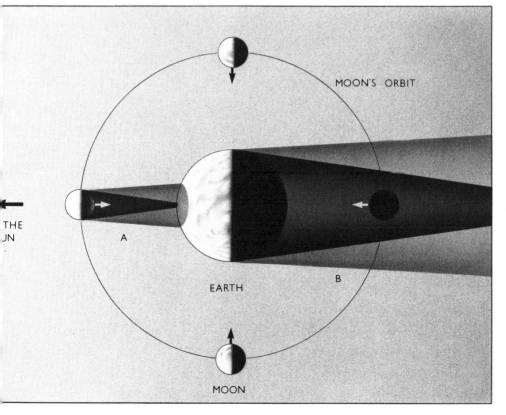

MOON'S ORBIT

THE
UN

A

EARTH

B

MOON

According to Bellamy, the approach of the Moon will cause volcanoes on Earth to erupt violently.

There are a few Independent Thinkers who achieve not only fame, but also some degree of official backing. Dr Velikovsky, to be discussed in the next chapter, was one. Another was Trofim Lysenko, a Russian student of evolution and heredity, whose peculiar theories were supported by the Soviet Government to the exclusion of all others, and who managed to put back the study of genetics in the U.S.S.R. by at least 30 years; even now it has not fully recovered, though Lysenko has long since fallen from grace (he died a few years ago). And the WEL cult, which was just as outlandish as anything that Velikovsky or Lysenko could conjure up, was backed quite seriously by the Nazis in Germany before World War II; at one stage the Government even had to issue an official statement to the effect that one could still be a good National Socialist without believing in cosmic ice! Moreover, there was one famous astronomer, Philip Fauth, who drew a large if inaccurate lunar map and became something of a convert, effectively ruining his scientific reputation in the process.

At its height, WEL probably had as many as a million supporters, most of them in Germany but quite a few in other countries as well, including England. After World War II, with the advent of space travel, it inevitably declined, and when Neil Armstrong took his famous 'one small step' on to the lunar Sea of Tranquillity without finding the need to equip himself with skates, the idea of an icy Moon died. Yet there are still some people who accept the theory that the Earth is spiralling towards destruction, and will come to an end when it makes its final dive into the solar flames.

In fact the Earth's path round the Sun is absolutely stable, so let us return to the Moon. Here we find a different situation. Instead of approaching us, the Moon is moving further away. The recession is not great, and amounts to only a few centimetres per year, but it brings us back to the whole idea of tidal friction and the Moon's trick of keeping the same face turned towards us all the time.

The Moon's revolution period round the Earth is 27.3 days. (To be pedantic, this is the time taken for the Earth and Moon to revolve round their common centre of gravity, but this point lies inside the Earth's globe, so for the moment we need not bother about it.) The axial rotation period of the Moon is also 27.3 days. This is really too much to be coincidental, and there is no mystery about it. Long ago, when the Solar System was young, the Moon is thought to have spun round much more quickly, but it was strongly affected by the gravitational pull of the Earth, which tended to cause a bulge in the Moon's still-viscous globe. As the Moon rotated, it had to fight against this force, and its spin was slowed down until, relative to the Earth, it had stopped altogether. The lunar rotation had become synchronous, or 'captured'.

Note that I say that the rotation had stopped 'relative to the Earth', which is not the same thing as saying that it had stopped altogether. Relative to the Sun, the Moon continues to spin round, so that day and night conditions are the same all over the surface; once the Sun rises over any particular region, it will not set again for a period equal to two terrestrial weeks, which is something that future colonists will find rather strange. Years ago I gave an analogy which I repeat here because I have never been able to think of anything better. Take a chair to represent the Earth, and let your head represent the Moon; your face is the familiar hemisphere, while the back of your head is 'the other side'. Now look at the chair and walk round it, turning as you go so as to keep your face turned chairward. After one circuit you will have faced every wall of the room, so that you will have turned once on your axis, but anyone sitting on the chair will never have seen the back of your neck. This is how the Moon behaves, and this is why we Earthbound mortals are permanently unable to see the far hemisphere.

(I admit that there are certain complications, and the Moon seems to rock very slowly to and fro, so that all in all we can examine a grand total of 59 per cent of the total surface; only 41 per cent is permanently out of view, but this is something which need not bother us now, because the basic principle is clear enough.)

There is another point to bear in mind. Just as the Earth slowed down the spin of the Moon, so the Moon is doing its best to retard the spin of the Earth. It is, of course, the chief tide-producing agent, and the friction of the water against the sea-bed has a definite effect. The days are getting longer. Not by much; neglecting random variations, each day is 0.00000002 seconds longer than its predecessor, which adds up to about one-fiftieth of a second every 1,000 years. You might think that this would be undetectable, but nowadays we have atomic clocks which are better timekeepers than the Earth. We can also see the effects when we come to study eclipse records of long ago.

Consider eclipses of the Sun. These occur when the new moon passes directly in front of the Sun, hiding it briefly; by a lucky chance (and here we really do have to assume that it is sheer coincidence) the Moon and the Sun appear about the same size in the sky, so that under suitable conditions the Moon can blot out the Sun completely. These solar eclipses were recorded by all the early peoples, and caused considerable alarm. The Chinese believed that a hungry dragon was trying to gobble up the Sun, which would certainly mean the end of the world; the obvious remedy was to shout, scream, beat gongs and drums, and make as much commotion as possible in order to scare the beast away. (It always worked, though there is a story, probably apocryphal, that two Court astrologers with the unlikely names of Hsi and Ho were executed because they had failed to predict an eclipse, thereby imperilling the Emperor and everybody else.) The Greeks were more scientific, and they timed the eclipses quite well. Working backwards, it is found that their timings do not agree with what might be expected, and this brings us back to the increase in the length of the day.

Are you ready for a little mathematics? I hope so, and I promise that it involves nothing more fearsome than simple multiplication and division. If you are as bad at mathematics as I am, you may skip the next paragraph, but I would urge you to try to follow me.

Each day is 0.00000002 seconds longer than the previous one. Therefore, a century ago (that is to say 36,525 days ago) the length of the day was shorter by 0.00073 seconds. Taking an average between then and now, the length of the day was half this value, or 0.00036 seconds, shorter than at present. But since 36,525 days have elapsed, the total error is 36,525 x 0.00036 = 13 seconds. Therefore, when we calculate back, the position of the Moon will be in error; it will seem to have moved too far, i.e. too fast. The discrepancy shows up when we consider eclipses which took place in classical times. Astronomers call it 'secular acceleration', and find that the difference between observation and calculation can amount to several hours. Moreover, eclipse records go back a long way. For instance, one was described in the inscription on a clay tablet found in the ruins of the ancient seaport of Ugarit, in what is now Syria. This eclipse happened in 1375 BC.

It is also known that the loss of energy caused by the slowing-down of the Earth is transferred to the Moon, which is why the Moon is edging outwards. Calculating forwards now instead of backwards, we find that in about the year AD 50,000 million the

Moon will have receded to 340,000 miles; it will then take 47 days to go round us, and this will also be the length of the Earth's axial rotation, so that inhabitants of one hemisphere will find the Moon permanently above the horizon, while dwellers in the other hemisphere will never see it at all.

But now a new factor emerges. The Moon is not the only tide-raiser; the Sun has an effect as well, and when the Moon has reached its maximum distance from us the solar tides will go on slowing down the Earth's spin. Everything is reversed. When the Earth's rotation has become longer than the Moon's revolution period, the Moon will start to come inwards again. Inexorably the approach will continue, until at last the Moon comes within the Roche limit, and is broken up by the Earth's gravity. It will shatter, first into large pieces and then into smaller ones; these remnants will be spread round the Earth, so that instead of having a large satellite we will have a system of rings. Even before this, huge tides will have swept over the lands, wiping out all life, while the crust of the Earth itself will have been breached. If the Moon is not disrupted, it will collide with the Earth and destroy both bodies, leaving nothing but a swarm of debris.

All this sounds plausible enough, and has been the subject of many technical investigations, but we now know that it can never happen, because the time scale is completely wrong. So far as we are concerned there can never be a year AD 50,000 million, because the Earth will not then exist; it will have been destroyed by changes in the energy output of the Sun, to be described in Chapter 9.

What, then, are the chances of a wandering body invading the Earth–Moon system, wrenching the Moon out of its stable orbit and sending it crashing earthwards? Again we must say that this is absolutely out of the question, and so the Moon is no threat. There have been some vastly entertaining stories about lunar collisons, notably R. C. Sherriff's *The Hopkins Manuscript* and Olaf Stapledon's classic *Last and First Men,* but they are fiction only, and have no scientific basis.

Yet the fears linger on. Not many years ago there was a minor panic in Brazil, caused by a radio announcer who had been dismissed for some reason or other, and who was feeling decidedly peeved with the authorities. When reading his final news bulletin, he calmly stated that astronomers had made a great discovery: the Moon was falling, and was due to land on the Earth within a couple of weeks. Quite a number of listeners believed him, and the radio station was besieged by callers who wanted to know what was the best course of action. I understand that the announcer became somewhat unpopular with his superiors, and this was definitely his last broadcast; but he had made his point, and for some weeks afterwards there were many Brazilians who kept their eyes turned skywards, hoping against hope that the Moon would not swell in size prior to landing in the jungle with an unpleasant thud.

Chapter Five

Comets of Doom

One night during the early part of 1973, Dr Lubos Kohoutek, a well-known Czechoslovakian astronomer working at the Hamburg Observatory in West Germany, discovered a comet. This, in the normal way, would not have been remarkable. Several comets are under observation every year, some of them bright enough to be seen in telescopes of moderate size; a new discovery is interesting, but in the ordinary course of events it provokes no discussion outside astronomical circles. However, Kohoutek's Comet was different. Though it looked like nothing more than a tiny smudge on the photographic plate, its movement showed that it was a very long way away. Its distance from us was over 400,000,000 miles, and few comets are visible as far out in the Solar System as that.

Therefore the comet was large, and when its orbit was worked out even non-astronomers started to become excited. Calculations showed that in November the comet's orbit would cross that of the Earth, though the Earth itself would be nowhere near the point of intersection and no collision would be possible. Predictions indicated that before the beginning of December we would be treated to a real spectacle – a comet almost as bright as the half-moon, with a tail stretching across the sky in the manner of a scimitar. At its perihelion, or closest approach to the Sun, it would be racing along at about 100 miles per second (as against the Earth's sluggish $18\frac{1}{2}$ miles per second), and in the middle of January 1974 it would brush past us at only 75,000,000 miles, still brilliant and imposing. Well before it drew close to the Earth's orbit it had been nicknamed 'the Comet of the Century'.

Alas, no astronomer is infallible, and comets are never reliable. Kohoutek's Comet moved exactly as forecast, but as a spectacle it proved to be a non-event. At its best it was visible with the naked eye

50

if you knew where to look for it, but that was all, and I had every sympathy with my old friend Bernard Levin, who wrote a bitter letter in the London *Times* accusing me of having stolen the comet for reasons of my own! People who had expected a display of cosmic pyrotechnics were sadly disappointed.

I mention Kohoutek's Comet because at the time when it was drawing inwards, and was still expected to become brilliant, astrologers and other end-of-the-worlders were in full cry. For instance, there was a lurid pamphlet entitled *The Christmas Monster*, written by a Mr Moses David and issued by a religious organization calling itself the Children of God, about whom I have no further information. The comet, wrote Mr David, was a sign of divine vengeance. Even if the world did not actually perish, there would be widespread damage, with storms, tempests and tremendous earthquakes. He also claimed that it would mark the downfall of 'Fascist America and its new Nazi Emperor'. Presumably he and his followers were somewhat chagrined when the comet turned out to be so puny, and natural disasters were conspicuous only by their absence.

Comets have always been regarded as unlucky, and the fear of them is not completely dead even yet, as Mr David's pamphlet showed. They have been responsible for several panics in historical times, and they were generally taken to be signs of divine displeasure. Basically, there were four causes of apprehension: nebulous fears of the astrological type, the destruction of the Earth by a head-on collision, a near miss which would tip the world sideways or else throw it out of its present orbit, and contamination of the atmosphere by poisonous cometary gases.

Ancient peoples had no idea of the true nature of comets, and tended to regard them as luminous phenomena in the upper air, but certainly they had an intense distrust of them. The Romans were of this opinion. I quote Tacitus, writing in AD 64: 'At the close of this year people discoursed only of prodigies, the forerunners of approaching calamaties; of thunderstorms more frequent than at any other epoch, and of a comet, a kind of presage that Nero always expiated with illustrious blood.' The Emperor Nero, who was ruler of Rome at the time, was not noted for his kindness and generosity; his reign was punctuated by several comets, so that historians such as Tacitus drew their own conclusions. Later, in AD 79, another bright comet appeared, but the current Emperor, Vespasian, was not alarmed: 'This hairy star does not concern me. It menaces rather the King of the Parthians, for he is hairy, while I am bald.' Alas, Vespasian was wrong. He died soon after the comet had faded from the sky.

All this is not the same as possible global destruction, but the overall fear of comets persisted for a long time. One famous description was given by the French doctor Ambroise Paré in 1528: 'This comet was so horrible, so frightful, and it produced such great terror that some died of fright and others fell sick. It appeared to be of extreme length, and was the colour of blood. At the summit of it was seen the figure of a bent arm, holding in its hand a great sword as though about to strike. At the end of the point there were three stars. On both sides of the rays of this comet there were seen a great number of axes, knives and blood-coloured swords, among which were a large number of hideous human faces, with beards and bristling hair.' Whether Dr Paré was actually describing a comet is not certain; he may have seen a brilliant display of aurora borealis or northern lights, and it is true that there are no other records of a comet in 1528, but it demonstrates the fear which comets inspired.

In Shakespeare's *Julius Caesar* we find the famous lines:

When beggars die, there are no comets seen;
The heavens themselves blaze forth the death of princes.

While Milton, in *Paradise Lost*, wrote:

Satan stood
Unterrified, and like a comet burn'd
That fires the length of Ophiuchus huge
In th' Artick sky, and from its horrid hair
Shakes pestilence and war.

Yet are there any scientific grounds for the dread of comets, and what would happen if we really did suffer a direct collision?

Brilliant though they may sometimes become, comets are flimsy, ethereal things. A large comet is made up of a nucleus, surrounded by a head or coma, and with a tail (or tails) streaming outwards. Most of the mass is concentrated in the nucleus, which is thought to be icy in nature, composed of what may be termed an icy conglomerate – that is to say, small solid particles held together in ices such as those of frozen ammonia, methane, carbon dioxide and water. Comets have been likened to dirty ice-balls, which may be unromantic but is certainly apt. Tails are of two main kinds: those composed of gas, and those which are made up of dust. These tails always point more or less away from the Sun, because they are repelled by 'solar wind', a constant stream of low-energy atomic particles sent out by the Sun in all directions. Therefore, when a comet is receding from the Sun, it travels tail first.

Not all comets have tails. Most of them look more like tiny pieces of luminous cotton wool in the sky, with no definite shape at all, and because they depend upon reflected sunlight they can be seen only when they are reasonably close to the Sun and the Earth. (As they near perihelion, they do emit a certain amount of light on their own account, but even so the Sun is directly responsible.) Cometary gas is extremely thin, and is millions of times less dense than the air that you and I are breathing, so that it can do us no harm, even though some of its constituents would be poisonous in greater quantity. Only the nucleus is dense enough to do damage, and it must be admitted that as yet our positive knowledge of cometary nuclei is very incomplete.

Most comets move round the Sun in very elliptical paths. Those which have periods of a few years must be regarded as old friends, and we always know when and where to expect them. Thus Encke's Comet (named after the last-century German astronomer Johann Encke, who was the first to work out its orbit) has a period of only 3.3 years, and has now been seen at over 50 different returns. But with one exception, Halley's, all the short-period or medium-period comets are faint, and the brilliant visitors seen now and then take so long to complete one journey round the Sun that they cannot be predicted. They were fairly frequent during the 19th century, but since then there has been a relative dearth of them. Of course, many of the fainter comets are also to all intents and purposes non-periodical, and Kohoutek's, for example, is not expected back for about 75,000 years. Meanwhile, there has been a recent theory due to two Edinburgh astronomers, Victor Clube and Bill Napier, which is relevant here, and is as unexpected as it is fascinating.

Most astronomers believe that comets are *bona-fide* members of the Solar System, and were produced from the 'solar nebula', a cloud of material associated with the youthful Sun. Clube and Napier do not agree. They think that comets are collected by the Sun during the passage through a vast interstellar cloud, so that there are definite epochs when the supply of comets is replenished.

This is logical enough, because even though there are plenty of comets around at the present time, they must be short-lived on the cosmical scale. Each time a comet nears the Sun it is heated, and some of its ices are evaporated to form the tail, so that after a definite number of returns to perihelion all the gas is exhausted; nothing remains but the nucleus, and according to one theory the comet then becomes an asteroid or minor planet. This is not to suggest that all asteroids are ex-comets; some of them are far too large and massive, and Ceres, the senior member of the swarm, has a diameter of over 600 miles. However, those asteroids which swing away from the main zone between Mars and Jupiter are in a different category, and I will have more to say about them later.

Clube and Napier have made exhaustive studies of old legends and myths, and believe that in the remote past a brilliant periodical comet, named by them the Cosmic Serpent, made periodical close approaches to the Earth. Parts of it broke away and landed, causing wide devastation. If this is correct, it would at least go a long way towards explaining the age-old fear of comets. Finally the Cosmic Serpent disintegrated; many other periodical comets collected by the Sun during its last passage through an interstellar cloud, ending about 10,000 years ago, have also disappeared, so that the total number of Solar System comets will not be restored until the next crossing of a cloud.

It is fair to say that many people are somewhat dubious about the theory, but it must be taken very seriously. A direct hit from a large comet-turned asteroid might well fracture the Earth's crust. Luckily, the chances against such a collision are very great.

The most famous of all comets is named in honour of Edmond Halley, a close friend of Isaac Newton, who became the second Astronomer Royal at Greenwich. Halley saw the comet in 1682, when it was a prominent naked-eye object, and found that its orbit was remarkably similar to those of comets seen previously in 1607 and in 1531. He reasoned that the three comets must be one and the same, with a period of 76 years, and he predicted that it would be seen once more in 1758. It was; on Christmas night of that year it was picked up by a Saxon amateur named Palitzsch, and since then it has returned in 1835 and 1910. It was recovered in 1982, and its next perihelion is due in February 1986.

It was during Halley's time that we come to the greatest of all comet scares. The man responsible, the Rev. Dr William Whiston, had made his reputation as a serious scientist, and when he published his remarkable book *A New Theory of the Earth*, in 1696, he was not howled down. The book was well received, and ran to several editions. Seven years later Whiston was appointed Lucasian Professor of Mathematics at Cambridge in succession to Newton, so that at that stage he can hardly have been regarded as an eccentric.

Whiston was born in 1667 in the village of Norton-juxta-Twycrosse, in Leicestershire. From all accounts his upbringing was extremely strict, since his father and all the members of his family were highly religious, and prayers and sermons continued for much of the day and night. Young Whiston may have been melancholy and neurotic, but he was academically brilliant, and when he went to Cambridge University at the age of 19 he soon earned a reputation as an excellent mathematician. (Later on he carried out some valuable researches, particularly in connection with the exact determination of longitude.) He graduated from Cambridge with honours, and in 1693 he was ordained, becoming Chaplain to Bishop Moore of Norwich. He was also made Vicar of Lowestoft-with-Kissingland at the munificent salary of £120 per year, and resigned only when he became Lucasian Professor in 1703. There seemed no reason whatsoever why he should not live out his life as a respected and serious academic.

Yet his *New Theory of the Earth* was not only unconventional, but wildly so, and he made the classic mistake of confusing comets with planets. He went so far as to claim that the Earth used to be a comet, with a path which took it close to the Sun, so that the present heat of the Earth's core is an aftermath of the high temperatures to which our luckless world was subjected during its cometary phase. When God decided that the time had come for Man to appear, the comet's path became less eccentric, so that the air was purified, oceans appeared, and the Earth changed from a comet into a planet . . . .

Even though comets were still regarded as mysterious objects at that period, it is hard to understand why his book was taken seriously. It was obvious, particularly to Newton and Halley, that the difference in mass between a comet and a planet is so vast that there can be no interchange of identity. True, comets may be large – the coma of the great comet of 1843, for instance, was bigger than the Sun – but by planetary standards their masses are absolutely negligible; it is rather like comparing a meringue with a cannonball. There have been observational proofs of this in more recent times. In 1770 Lexell's Comet, admittedly one of the smaller specimens, passed within 750,000 miles of the Earth, so that it was visible with the naked eye, and the French mathematician Laplace pointed out that if the comet had been as massive as the Earth our 'day' would have been shortened by almost three hours. Of course there was no effect at all, and Laplace found that the mass of the comet could not have been more than 1/5000 of that of the Earth (actually it was much less than that). Subsequently, Lexell's Comet had the temerity to approach mighty Jupiter, and invaded the Jovian satellite system. Neither Jupiter nor its moons showed any effects, but the comet's orbit was so violently twisted that it was completely changed, and astronomers lost track of it. No doubt the comet still exists, but we have no idea where it is now.

Quite apart from this fundamental error, Whiston's theories were hardly scientific. He concentrated upon a bright comet which had been seen in 1680, and to which Edmond Halley had (wrongly) assigned a period of 575 years. God, said Whiston, had always had an uneasy feeling that Man might be prone to sin, and so he had fashioned the 1680 comet as an agent of punishment. Indeed, it had already been in action: on either 28 November 1349 BC or 2 December 2926 BC, the comet approached the Earth, and by-passed us within 9,000 miles. Assuming that the comet had a mass one-quarter that of the Earth (!), Whiston claimed that the effect was to produce a huge tide not only in the oceans, but also in the lands. Water swirled around, mountains were broken apart, and much of the world was covered by a flood more than six miles deep, so that almost every man, woman and beast came to an untimely end. Need I add that this was nothing more nor less than the Biblical Deluge? The head and tail of the rampaging comet actually struck the Earth, and discharged so much water that rain kept on falling for 40 days and 40 nights. Finally God decided that since there were so few people left – only Noah and his nearest and dearest – it might be as well to give *homo sapiens* a second chance. The comet receded, the water-level fell, and the Earth became habitable again; the doors of the Ark opened, and the situation reverted to normal.

Unfortunately Man had not learned his lesson. Before long there was new evidence of sin, and the comet was still lurking in the background, ready for a further onslaught if need be. Whiston held that it would soon come back, and that this time there would be no half-measures. The best description I have found was given later by the French astronomer Pingré, and it is worth quoting here, because it is so vivid:

'Hardly can the mouth of a volcano vomiting forth lava liquified by the interior consuming heat give an idea of the fiery atmosphere of the comet. The air will then interpose no obstacle to the activity of this central fire; on the contrary, the inflamed particles with which our atmosphere will be charged, carried down by their own weight into the half-open bowels of the Earth, will powerfully augment the action of the central fire. The comet will even separate the Moon from the Earth, and affect the diurnal and annual motion of the Earth by rendering both these movements equal, and by destroying besides the eccentricity of the Earth's orbit, which will again become circular as before the Flood. Lastly, after the saints have reigned a thousand years on Earth, itself regenerated by fire and rendered habitable anew by Divine will, the comet will again strike the Earth, the terrestrial orbit will be excessively elongated, and the Earth, once more a comet, will cease to be habitable.'

This did not sound at all promising, but Whiston was confident that there could be no mistake. The only point at issue was – When? 1715 was one possibility, but when that year passed by with no alarms or excursions Whiston checked his calculations and found that the end would certainly come in 1736.

Meanwhile his own career had taken a turn for the worse, not because of his preoccupation with the comet but for much more immediate reasons. His religious views were not conventional, and in 1708 he was accused of Arianism. Few people will know what Arianism is (I didn't, until I looked it up). It is, in fact, an early theological heresy, teaching that God is utterly isolated and separate from the beings he has created. Whiston was violently attacked by his clerical colleagues but, being Whiston, he declined to retract. Instead he published a book called *Primitive Christianity Reviewed*, which only made matters worse. Inevitably, he was asked to resign as Lucasian Professor, and when he refused to do so he was dismissed. He was even prosecuted for heresy, and though nothing came of it he retired in dudgeon to a farm in Suffolk, where he continued both his useful scientific work and his calculations about the approaching Day of Judgement in which his faith never wavered.

Eventually he seems to have decided that the end would come on 16 October 1736. He predicted that a comet would appear (not the 1680 one, presumably, but another dispatched specifically for the purpose); the Second Coming would be timed for the previous day, and the final destruction would be in a holocaust of fire and brimstone. At this stage the story becomes rather confused. There are reports that three days before his scheduled Day of Doom he gave a public lecture in London in which he broadcast his warning, allowing his hearers sufficient time to repent. Certainly there was something of a local panic; people started streaming out of the City, though just why they should have regarded the surrounding countryside as safer is not clear. It is even on record that the Archbishop of Canterbury felt bound to issue a public disclaimer.

I have been unable to find any really reliable reports of what went on, and the terror was short lived. The Day of Judgement was again postponed, Whiston went back to Suffolk, and that was that. Whiston lived on until 1752, still confident that the comet would return. Nowadays it is thought that the comet of 1680 has a period of at least 8,000 years, in which case we have a long reprieve.

You might imagine that the idea of comets changing into planets, or vice versa, would have died with Whiston. Not so! In 1950 there came *Worlds in Collision*, by a Russian-born, American-based psychoanalyst named Immanuel Velikovsky, which was decidedly Whistonian in character. This time the planet Jupiter suffered a tremendous outburst, and expelled a comet which subsequently turned into the planet Venus. Initially it bounced around the cosmos rather in the manner of a celestial ping-pong ball, and it had several traumatic encounters with the Earth. One of these occurred when the Israelites were crossing the Red Sea. The pull of the comet stopped the Earth's rotation at a convenient moment, and allowed the party to cross from one shore to the other without getting their feet wet. Later the comet returned, showering down the manna which provided enough food to last for 40 years. It then had a near-encounter with Mars, and had its tail chopped off; Mars itself approached the Earth, and scored a near-miss in 687 BC. Various other encounters took place, suitably linked with events in the Old Testament, and so on.

All this is great fun, and the Biblical references are absolutely correct. Neither could there be any doubt about Velikovsky's sincerity. He became something of a cult figure in the United States, and amassed a considerable following. But to the best of my knowledge he never gave a definite date for the end of the world, so that he does not concern us further here.

Going back in time once more, we come to the year 1773, and a paper by the great French mathematician Lalande called (in translation) *Reflections on those Comets which can approach the Earth*. Lalande's paper sparked off a curious panic which affected not only Paris, but also much of France. According to rumour, a comet would collide with the Earth on 20 or 21 May, with cataclysmic results. Lalande had not, of course, suggested anything of the kind, so by early May he felt compelled to issue a clarification, but his letter, published in the *Gazette de France*, had an effect opposite to what had been intended; many people jumped to the conclusion that he was trying to hide the truth. One man who was not taken in was the famous writer Francois-Marie Arouet Voltaire, who set to work and produced a *Letter on the Pretended Comet*, which appeared on 17 May. In it he commented that 'certain Parisians . . . expect a comet, which is to take our little globe from behind and reduce it to impalpable powder, according to a certain prediction of the Academy of Sciences which has not yet been made'. But 'the Parisians will not desert their city on 20 May; they will sing their songs, and the play *The Comet and the End of the World* will be performed at the Opéra-Comique'.

Yet the alarm spread, and some members of the clergy took advantage of it. They announced that they had been allotted preferential tickets for seats in Paradise, and proceeded to sell them at high prices. I am not sure how many were sold, but it must have been a considerable number. History does not relate whether any of the buyers subsequently got their money back.

France was again the scene of the next comet scare, which occurred in 1832. This time the culprit was a comet which later became notorious for an entirely different reason. It had originally been found in 1772 by Charles Messier, who was one of the most successful of all comet hunters, and who made many discoveries, though he is best remembered today for his catalogue of star-clusters and the misty-looking objects which we term nebulæ and galaxies. The comet was not brilliant, but it was easy to locate, and its orbit was calculated by a German named Friedrich Bessel, who found that it had a period of $6\frac{3}{4}$ years. The next few returns passed unnoticed, but Bessel predicted that the comet would be seen again in 1826, and on 27 February that year it was picked up by an Austrian soldier, Captain Wilhelm von Biela, who was a skilful amateur astronomer. We remember it today as Biela's Comet.

The next return was scheduled for 1832, and in France yet another eminent mathematician, Damoiseau, found that its orbit would cut that of the Earth on 29 October. He was quite right, but the repercussions were startling. Once more the alarm was spread; newspaper headlines proclaimed that the Earth would be smashed into tiny fragments, and that there was little that anyone could do about it.

There was, however, one fact which the newspapers had overlooked, but which was pointed out by François Arago, the leading French astronomer of the time. Certainly the orbit of Biela's Comet would intersect that of the Earth – but the Earth would be nowhere near the cutting-point at the time. Arago found that the minimum distance between the Earth and the comet would be over 49,000,000 miles. But things were by now out of control, and according to a later account, written by an author named Mackay, 'the greatest alarm spread over the continent of Europe, lest the comet, whose appearance was then foretold by astronomers, should destroy the Earth. Many persons refrained from undertaking or concluding any business during that year.'

Biela's Comet came and went without incident. It was missed at the return of 1839, because it was unfavourably placed for observation; at its return in 1846 it split into two parts, and the twins came back once more in 1852, but that was their swan-song. They have never been seen since, though their remnants have been observed in the form of a shower of meteors or shooting-stars. Other old periodical comets have vanished just as effectively, but Biela's is the classic case of a comet death.

I have already mentioned the great comet of 1843, which was really brilliant, and which appeared at the climax of the Millerite scare, though William Miller himself had not necessarily expected it, and had relied entirely upon his Biblical calculations. Then, in 1857, a German writer whose name I have failed to unearth announced that a fiery comet would destroy the world on 13 June; there were various apprehensive comments, but, predictably, nothing happened. Four years later the Earth passed harmlessly through the tail of a great comet, but the only visible result was a slight luminosity of the sky on the night of 30 June 1861, and even

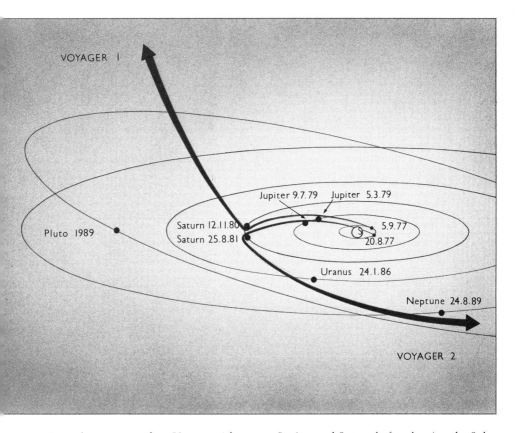

ABOVE: Interplanetary snooker. Voyager 1 bypasses Jupiter and Saturn before leaving the Solar System for good; Voyager 2 takes in Uranus and Neptune as well.
BELOW: Monsieur Jacot's theory, in which the planets take part in what can only be described as a cosmic equivalent of musical chairs.

A menacing comet heads for Earth, its brilliant tail strung out behind it as it moves inwards, with the obvious intention of scoring a bull's eye.

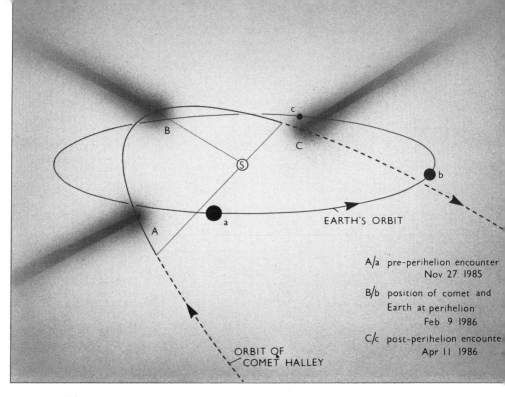

A/a pre-perihelion encounter
Nov 27 1985

B/b position of comet and
Earth at perihelion
Feb 9 1986

C/c post-perihelion encounter
Apr 11 1986

EARTH'S ORBIT

ORBIT OF
COMET HALLEY

ABOVE: Halley's comet in 1986; sadly, it will not put on one of its best displays and is in no danger of being denounced by the Pope as an evil omen.
BELOW: The great comet of 1811, noted for its brilliance and the straightness of its long tail.

this rests upon very uncertain evidence. The distance between the Earth and the comet's head was about 11,000,000 miles, so that the danger was nil.

There was yet another 'comet scare' in France in 1857, caused this time not by a brilliant visitor, but by a comet which never appeared at all. It was sparked off, quite unintentionally, by two reputable astronomers, Richard Dunthorne in England and A. Pingré in France. Dunthorne calculated the orbits of the bright comets seen in 1264 and 1566, and came to the conclusion that they might be identical. Accordingly, Pingré predicted a return for about 1848. Subsequently, he revised this to some time between 1856 and 1860, because of the gravitational effects of Saturn and Neptune which had not previously been taken into account.

This was by no means sensational; but then a German astrologer, whose name has not survived, announced that the comet would not only come back in 1857, but would collide with the Earth on 13 June. For some reason or other panic started, confined mainly though not entirely to Paris. A correspondent there wrote that 'For a fortnight we have not been able to step out without hearing the cry, "Here is the end of the World! A full description of the comet of June 13!" Women have miscarried; crops have been neglected; a cometary life insurance company (premiums payable in advance) was set up . . .' Prophets of doom were much in evidence. Not everyone took it seriously; there was a superb series of cartoons on the subject by the caricaturist Honoré Daumier, and leading astronomers of the time were not impressed. But not until 13 June was well past did the panic die away. Actually no bright comet appeared in 1857; 1858 saw the visit of Donati's Comet, which, with its magnificent tails, was possibly the most beautiful ever observed, but this time nobody in Paris was alarmed.

The return of Halley's Comet in 1910 did not produce anything in the nature of a major panic, though one enterprising manufacturer in Dallas, Texas, made a handsome sum of money by selling what he called comet pills. Then there was a disturbance in South America in 1944, when a Chilean astronomer named Munos Ferradas announced that a comet would strike the Earth some time in August. People in both Chile and Bolivia made for the hills, and stayed there until they were satisfied that the danger was over. Actually, no major comet was seen at any time in 1944, and there have been only a few since, though the prominent naked-eye

Bennett's Comet of 1970 was mistaken by some Arabs for an Israeli war weapon.

I must, however, mention another very recent rumour, which was featured in a few daily papers even though it led to no general alarm. This concerns one of the more interesting members of the comet family, named Swift-Tuttle after its two discoverers.

Comet Swift-Tuttle was first seen in 1862. It was not brilliant, though it was visible with the naked eye and had a considerable tail. A few years later the celebrated Italian astronomer Giovanni Virginio Schiaparelli (best remembered today, perhaps, for his drawings of Mars, which he believed to be covered with a network of canals) made some valuable calculations showing that the comet was intimately linked with the Perseid meteor shower which is seen every August. Meteors are tiny particles, usually smaller than grains of sand, moving round the Sun; if a meteor happens to dash into the top of the Earth's resisting atmosphere it rubs against the air-particles, and burns away, producing the effect known to us as a shooting-star. Many meteors move round the Sun in shoals, so that every time the Earth plunges through a shoal we see a shower of shooting-stars. The Perseids are the most reliable; normally the shower begins around 27 July and does not end until 17 August, with a maximum on 12 August. If you stare up into a dark, moonless sky for a few minutes at any time during the first fortnight of August, you will be very unlucky not to see at least a couple of shooting-stars. The meteors seem to radiate from a position in the constellation of Perseus, which is why they have been so named.

Schiaparelli calculated that the orbit of the Perseid shoal was practically the same as that of Comet Swift-Tuttle. This could not be due to coincidence, and it proved something which had long been suspected: meteors are simply cometary debris. Records of the Perseids go back to AD 36, and ever since about 830 it has been noted almost every year, though it was not until 1835 that its existence as a definite shower was recognized by two astronomers, A. Quételet in Belgium and E. C. Herrick in the United States.

Mathematical work indicated that Comet Swift-Tuttle itself had a period of 120 years, so that it would be due back once more in 1982 or thereabouts. Several writers suggested that it might collide with the Earth, causing widespread damage, but careful work by a British-born, American-based expert, Dr Brian Marsden, showed that a collision could occur only if the comet reached perihelion on

12 August precisely. Even if this happened, the chances were still very great that the comet would miss us by a million miles at least. Marsden concluded that the danger of a direct hit was so slight that it could be discounted, so that there was no cause for alarm even though the comet had not been observed for over a century and its exact position was unknown. At the time of writing (March 1983) the comet has not turned up.

Can comets be dismissed as entirely harmless? According to two of the world's most eminent astronomers, Professor Sir Fred Hoyle and Dr Chandra Wickramasinghe, the answer is 'no'. In 1978 they published a book in which they assumed that collisions with comets release viruses into our atmosphere, and that these viruses have unpleasant effects, producing epidemics ranging from influenza to smallpox. They even go so far as to claim that life originated well away from the Earth, and was brought here by a comet. Again we have a theory which represents a minority view, but which must not be dismissed out of hand. However, it does not involve the physical destruction of the Earth, and so does not concern us here. We must range further afield.

Chapter Six

Cosmic Bullets

WORLD DISASTER MISSED BY THREE HOURS . . . EARTH'S NARROW ESCAPE AS TINY PLANET PLUNGES BY. Such was a newspaper headline which greeted me one morning in late 1937. Other papers were hardly less sensational, and you might have been forgiven for supposing that the Earth was under a constant threat of cosmic bombardment.

In fact there really had been an encounter with a dwarf planet. The visitor was called Hermes (that was the name given to it by its discoverer, the German astronomer Karl Reinmuth), and it had scraped by at a mere 485,000 miles, which is less than twice the distance of the Moon. True, it was only about a mile in diameter, but its mass amounted to many millions of tons, and it would have caused havoc if it had landed upon a city. The newspaper headline was based on the revelation that if Hermes had crossed the Earth's orbit three hours earlier it might have scored a bull's-eye upon Leningrad. Actually, things are not really so simple as this, and neither Leningrad nor any other city was in danger, but the hectic fly-by of Hermes did do a good deal to swing attention back to the possibility of asteroid collisions. Yet what precisely is meant by an 'asteroid'? There are several classes of objects which could be potential sources of danger, and the distinction between them is not so clear as was believed only a few years ago, so let us examine the problem a little more closely. We must consider the following:

1. *Comets, already discussed.* The only part of a comet which is massive enough to do real damage is the nucleus. But when a comet has exhausted all its gas, it may assume the guise of –

2. *An exceptional asteroid, such as Hermes.* It is worth noting that two periodical comets, known as Neujmin 2 and Arend-

Rigaux, seem to have achieved this transformation during the past few decades, since they now look absolutely stellar. If this idea is correct (and it is supported by many experts, including Clube and Napier), there is an essential difference between a Hermes-type asteroid and a member of the main asteroid swarm, which is restricted to the region between the orbits of Mars and Jupiter. We also have –

3. *Meteorites, which are quite distinct from shooting-star meteors or cometary debris.* A meteorite is a solid body which comes from space and lands on the Earth; during its time spent in orbit round the Sun it should really be termed a meteoroid, but let us not confuse matters any more than is necessary. The real problem is to decide upon the dividing-lines between meteorites, asteroids and dead comets, and in this connection it may be appropriate to say something about an object which may possibly have belonged to any of the three classes. It came down at 7.17 p.m., local time, on 30 June 1908 in the Tunguska region of Siberia.

Tunguska is not a thickly-populated area. It is in fact virtually uninhabited except for wandering tribesmen, which was fortunate on this occasion, because nobody was killed. (Incidentally, there is no reliable record of a fatality caused by a tumbling meteorite, though one or two people have had narrow escapes.) Shortly after 7.15 p.m. on 30 June, a brilliant object shot across the sky of Western China. It seems to have been brighter than the Sun, so that not even the most myopic observer could have overlooked it. Flashing over the Mongolian border, it descended quickly, and crashed down among the pine-forests of Siberia, blowing trees flat over a wide area and producing what was described as a pillar of fire visible hundreds of miles away. In the trading post of Vanavara, 40 miles at least from the impact point, the blast of heat was terrifying, and a few seconds later a shock wave ripped through the village, damaging many houses and breaking practically every window. One witness, S. Semenov, wrote: 'I was sitting in my porch facing north when suddenly, to the north-west, there appeared a great flash of light. There was so much heat that my shirt was scorched on my back. I saw a huge fireball that covered a great part of the sky. . . . Then it became dark, and at the same time I felt an explosion that threw me several feet from the porch.' Earthquake-recording stations in various countries observed shocks, and there were also meteorological disturbances. Almost 400 miles from the impact site, doors and windows in the station of Kansk, on the Trans-Siberian railway, rattled violently, while an approaching train was so badly jolted that the driver pulled up hastily to make sure that there had been no damage to the engine or track. Obviously, something very exceptional had happened.

Tunguska is one of the most desolate regions of Siberia. Partly because of this, and partly because of the internal disorders in Russia, no expeditions reached the site for a long time. The man who finally decided to tackle the mystery was a geologist, Leonid Kulik, who had studied at St Petersburg, now Leningrad, and had become a forester. He was interested in meteorites, and Tunguska fascinated him, but he had to bide his time. For a* while the Bolsheviks imprisoned him as a suspected counter-revolutionary, which was true enough. Then came World War I, and it was not until 1927 that Kulik managed to make his way to the scene of the explosion. When he did, he saw plenty of evidence of devastation. Not only were pine-trees still lying flat, like matchsticks, but it was very clear that there had been a colossal blast of heat. What Kulik did not find was any evidence of meteoritic material, and he was equally unsuccessful on later expeditions; he never lost interest, and continued his studies up to the outbreak of World War II, which unfortunately he did not survive. In 1944 he was captured by the Germans, and died in a prison camp.

Neither has anyone else found meteorite fragments in the area, which opens up all sorts of possibilities. Weird theories were proposed, notably by a Russian science-fiction writer named Alexander Kazantsev, who maintained that the root cause was a nuclear blast. Flying saucer enthusiasts claimed that the missile was a visiting spaceship which made a forced landing and then blew up, while others suggested that the so-called meteorite might have been composed of 'anti-matter', so that when it came into contact with the Earth it was promptly annihilated.

A more logical explanation was offered by K. Florensky and other Soviet scientists. If the missile were the head of a small comet, the material would be icy; the tremendous frictional heat set up during the plunge downwards through the atmosphere would vaporize the ices, and on impact the whole missile would be destroyed, leaving no traces of meteoritic fragments or anything else. It has even been proposed that the object came from Encke's periodical comet. At any rate, the most recent major impact, which happened in 1947 in the general area of Vladivostok, was certainly due to a meteorite, because hundreds of fragments were collected. Again the region was uninhabited, and there were no casualties, but many small craters were produced.

Most museums have meteorite collections. You will see plenty, for instance, in the Geological Museum in South Kensington and in the National Maritime Museum at Greenwich, while if you happen to visit the Hayden Planetarium in New York you will see a true monster, weighing 36 tons, found by the explorer Peary in Greenland and laboriously transported to its present home. The holder of the heavyweight record is still lying where it fell in prehistoric times, near Grootfontein in South-West Africa; its estimated weight is at least 60 tons.

The most perfect example of a terrestrial meteorite crater is in Arizona, not so very far from the Lowell Observatory at Flagstaff. Its diameter is almost a mile, and it has become a noted tourist attraction. I recommend you to visit it if you are anywhere within range, though I warn you that if you scramble down to the bottom you will find that climbing up the wall again, under a broiling Arizonan sun, is decidedly exhausting.

There is absolutely no doubt that the Arizona crater is meteoritic, and many fragments have been collected. Its age is believed to be about 22,000 years, so that the fall took place long before there were any local astronomers to observe it, and Red Indian legends about 'fire descending from heaven' are of relatively modern manufacture. According to well-informed estimates, the meteorite was about 90 feet in diameter, though the solid mass which finally impacted had been reduced by 10 feet or so. The velocity as the meteorite landed was about 30,000 m.p.h., and the explosion was equivalent to half a million tons of T.N.T., devastating the country over a range of at least 100 miles. On impact, 90 per cent of the missile was vaporized; the remaining 10 per cent is buried under the southeastern rim of the crater. All animal and vegetable life in the danger-zone must have been instantly wiped out.

Other meteorite craters are known, a good example being that at Wolf Creek in Australia, but it is always wise to keep an open mind, as it seems that some alleged impact craters given in official lists are in fact volcanic – such as the Vredefort Ring in South Africa, some way from Pretoria. It is by no means so imposing as the Arizona

Crater, because the walls are low and in places reduced to clumps of hills, while two villages – Parys, and Vredefort itself – lie on the crater floor, but when seen from the air it is distinctive enough. Geologists who have made exhaustive studies of it are convinced that it was caused by internal forces rather than a meteorite strike because it fits in so neatly with the geology of the area.

Other worlds, too, have surface craters which may be relevant here. The Moon is the obvious example; any small telescope will show hundreds upon hundreds of walled circular formations, ranging from tiny pits up to colossal enclosures well over 150 miles in diameter. Many astronomers maintain that these are impact structures, with vulcanism playing a very minor role. I beg to differ; but in any case there can be no doubt that craters of both kinds are to be found on the Moon, just as they are on the Earth.

Recent results from unmanned spacecraft, such as the Vikings to Mars and the Voyagers to Jupiter and Saturn, have extended our range enormously. Mars has craters, both impact and volcanic; the highest volcano, Olympus Mons, towers to 15 miles above the outer country, and is topped by a 40-mile crater of the type known as a caldera, so that it is essentially similar to our own Mauna Loa and Mauna Kea in Hawaii, though it is very much larger and more massive. Attending Mars are two satellites, Phobos and Deimos, which were discovered in 1877 by Asaph Hall using a very large telescope, and which, from Earth, look like tiny points of light. The spacecraft have told us that both are irregular in shape, and that even Phobos, the larger of the two, has a longest diameter of no more than 30 miles, so that they are very different in nature from our own massive Moon. Quite possibly they come from the main asteroid belt, and were captured by Mars in the remote past. Each is cratered, and one structure on Phobos is so large that if it had been produced by a violent impact, Phobos itself would have been in definite danger of disruption.

Craters also exist on some of the satellites of Jupiter, but of more immediate interest to us is Tethys, one of the members of Saturn's system. It is about 630 miles in diameter, and appears to be made up of almost pure ice. On it there is a vast crater some 300 miles across. It is indeed hard to believe that this can have been due to a plunging missile, and the same is true for a very large crater on Mimas, one of the smaller satellites in the Saturnian family. Opinions differ, but there are at least reasons for looking very carefully at cratered surfaces before jumping to the conclusion that meteoric impact has been the chief agent.

This has been something of a digression. At least there is no doubt that if the Earth were hit by a major asteroid the results would be fatal, so let us dispose of these worldlets without further ado. In particular, are they themselves the remains of an old planet (or planets) which was broken up?

I must here say a little about Bode's Law, because it led to a systematic search for a new planet way back in the 18th century. It may or may not be a true Law; personally I doubt it, and neither should it be called after Johann Elert Bode, because it was originally worked out by a Wittenberg astronomer named Titius, and Bode merely popularized it. It came to general notice in 1772, and attracted a great deal of attention. Briefly, it is a mathematical relationship linking the distances of the various planets from the Sun, and it works like this:

Take the numbers 0, 3, 6, 12, 24, 48 and 96, each of which (apart from 3) is double its predecessor. Now add 4 to each. Taking the distance between the Earth and the Sun as 10 units, the other figures give the distances of the remaining planets from the Sun with fair accuracy. Hence:

Planet	Distance by Bode's Law	Real distance
Mercury	4	3.9
Venus	7	7.2
Earth	10	10 (because we made it so)
Mars	16	15.2
?	28	–
Jupiter	52	52.0
Saturn	100	95.4

Postponing any discussion of the question-mark corresponding to Bode's 28, the agreement is not at all bad. Then, in 1781, William Herschel discovered the planet Uranus, which moves far beyond Saturn. The Bode distance for it should have been 196. Actually it was 191.8; again fairly good, and many people became confident that the Law was something more than sheer coincidence. However, the problem of No. 28 remained, and Bode suggested that there ought to be a planet there, even though a small one, moving round the Sun outside the orbit of Mars and inside that of the first of the giants, Jupiter.

69

The cudgels were taken up by six observers who called themselves the 'Celestial Police'. There were headed by Johann Schröter, who had a great reputation as an expert in all matters concerning the Solar System, and a Hungarian baron with the exotic name of Franz Xavier von Zach. In 1800 they decided to divide up the sky into various sections, each 'policeman' being responsible for one section. Ironically, they were forestalled. At Palermo, in the island of Sicily, the Director of the Observatory, Piazzi, was busy making a new star catalogue when he happened upon a starlike object which moved against its background from night to night. Obviously it could not be a real star, and, sure enough, it proved to be the planet corresponding to Bode's number 28; the distance was found to be equivalent to 27.7. Piazzi christened it Ceres, after the patron goddess of Sicily.

The only trouble was that Ceres seemed to be disconcertingly small. We now know that its diameter is about 650 miles, and until recently it was thought to be even smaller than that. Even our Moon is over 2,000 miles across, and the Celestial Police regarded Ceres as frankly disappointing. Could there be any more worlds in the same region of the Solar System? They searched, and within the next decade they had identified three more, now called Pallas, Juno and Vesta. All were smaller than Ceres, and they became collectively known as minor planets, planetoids or asteroids. No others seemed to be forthcoming, and the Celestial Police disbanded – partly because Schröter's observatory at Lilienthal, near Bremen, was destroyed by the invading French soldiers in 1814, and the brass-tubed telescopes were looted because the soldiers believed them to be made of gold.

However, this was only the beginning. Asteroid No. 5, Astræa, was discovered in 1845 by a German postmaster-astronomer named Hencke, who had been searching tirelessly for over 13 years. Others followed. Today, more than 2,000 have been observed sufficiently well to have their orbits worked out, and the entire swarm may contain at least 40,000 members, though most of them are very small, and Ceres is much the most massive member of the swarm – indeed, it contains more than half the mass of all the asteroids put together. Of the rest, only Pallas and Vesta are as much as 300 miles in diameter. Some of the asteroids are believed to be stony in composition, while others contain considerable quantities of iron. The mass of Psyche, the largest-known iron-type asteroid, is believed to be about 50,000 million tons, though we cannot hope to be at all precise.

If Bode's Law is truly valid, there seems little escape from the conclusion that a relatively large planet did once exist in the present-day asteroid zone, and was shattered in some way – and if this can happen to any planet of the Solar System, it could presumably happen to the Earth as well. However, there are various weak points in the whole theory. In 1846 the planet Neptune was discovered as a result of some masterly calculations made by a French astronomer named Urbain Jean Joseph Le Verrier, later Director of the Paris Observatory, and according to repute one of the rudest men who has every lived. (One of his colleagues commented that although Le Verrier might not be the most detestable man in France, he was certainly the most detested.) Le Verrier's calculations, and also those made independently by an Englishman, John Couch Adams, showed where the new planet might be; the key to the problem was provided by Uranus, which persistently wandered away from its expected path and was therefore presumably being tugged out of position by some unknown body. Neptune turned out to be a giant planet, slightly more massive than Uranus. Its distance on the Bode scale should have been 388, as you can easily show if you care to do a little arithmetic. Yet the true distance proved to be only 300.7, so that Bode's Law breaks down completely.

Once a Law fails in an important case, it is no longer a Law. Bode's comes into this class, and I have always tended to consider it in the same light as one of those 'take-away-the-number-you-first-thought-of' games. If so, then there is no longer any need to assume the former existence of a large planet between Mars and Jupiter, and most astronomers now believe that the asteroids were simply left over, so to speak, when the principal planets were formed. Certainly there is no chance whatsoever that the larger members of the swarm can leave the main zone, and so from them we are safe. We come, at last, to the maverick asteroids, which, as we have seen, may well be the nuclei of defunct comets.

The breakthrough was made in 1898 by Witt, of Berlin, who discovered an asteroid which had an exceptional path. It is No. 433 in the list, and Witt named it Eros. It is shaped rather like a sausage, with a longer diameter of 18 miles, and it comes well within the orbit of Mars; at times, as in 1931 and 1975, it approaches the

Earth to within a distance of roughly 16,000,000 miles. This is still 60 times as remote as the Moon, but much closer than any of the main planets (Venus, not Mars as so many people think). It takes one and three quarter years to go round the Sun, and at its aphelion, or furthest point, it goes out beyond Mars.

Gradually other exceptional asteroids began to come to light: No. 719 (Albert) in 1911, 887 (Alinda) in 1918 and so on. All were small, and Albert has been lost altogether, so that we have little chance of relocating it except by pure luck. In 1932 another midget, Apollo, came within 7,000,000 miles; it was succeeded in 1936 by Adonis (less than 2,000,000 miles) and then, on 30 October 1937, by Hermes which, as I have said, hurtled by at a mere 485,000 miles.

Though there was no public alarm, and in any case the news about Hermes was not announced until the closest approach was over, it was suggested that sooner or later we might be hit by an asteroid. To date this has not happened, in historical times at least. Hermes retains the holder of the near-approach record, and only one other asteroid has been known to come within 1,000,000 miles. This was 1976 UA, not yet named, which by-passed us on 20 October of that year at approximately 740,000 miles. I must also mention No. 1685, Toro, which was discovered in 1948 and has been so well observed that it is not likely to be lost. Inaccurate press reports suggested that it might be a second satellite moving round the Earth, but this is not so; it travels round the Sun in the conventional way, and its distance from the Earth is always more than 1,000,000 miles.

Asteroids whose orbits cross that of the Earth are known as Apollo-type objects, after the best-known member of the class. There are even a few asteroids whose orbits lie entirely within that of the Earth; the picturesquely-named Ra-Shalom is one. The numbers of known close-approach asteroids are increasing rapidly, and it has become clear that they are much more plentiful than was believed a few years ago. For instance, consider the night of 28 February 1982. Two new 'Earth-grazers' were discovered within a few hours. At the Observatory of La Silla, in Chile, H. E. Schuster detected the still-unnamed 1982 DV; it was then 14,000,000 miles away from us, and since its diameter is little over a mile it was a faint object. Its orbit carries it from the main swarm almost as close-in as the Earth's orbit, but it does not actually cross, so that it is an

'Amor-type' asteroid and not an Apollo. The second discovery, 1982 DB, was found by Mrs E. Helin at Palomar in California; it is only about half a mile across, but when its path was worked out it was found to have crossed the Earth's orbit in December 1981 and again in February 1982. When Mrs Helin identified it, it was already over 9,000,000 miles from us, and receding rapidly, but it will certainly come back, as will other Earth-grazers such as Dædalus, Cerberus, Sisyphus and Quetzalcoatl. (Some of these allotted names are fascinating, but to discuss them here would be too much of a digression!)

I must also mention Icarus, discovered by the late Walter Baade as long ago as 26 June 1949. Its orbit is well known by now, and it is unique because at perihelion it passes within the orbit of Mercury, so that it must then be red hot. At aphelion it moves out to 183,000,000 miles, well into the main asteroid zone, so that it will be intensely cold. Icarus must have the most uncomfortable climate in the Solar System – a kind of cosmic Devil's Island. Despite its small size, it must weigh over 4,000 million tons, so that if it struck us it would do immense damage. Luckily, at the present epoch it cannot come closer than about 4,000,000 miles, as it did in 1968 and will do again in 1987. But if we were hit by Icarus or an asteroid of comparable size, what then?

Remember, asteroids are not fragile bodies, so that they would be able to drop right through the atmosphere and land more or less intact. On impact, the kinetic energy of the asteroid's movement would be changed into heat, scorching everything over a wide area, and the missile might well penetrate the Earth's crust, thereby converting itself into a very effective bomb. Material would be hurled miles above the ground; if the crust were broken there would be devastating earthquakes, while if the asteroid plunged into the sea it would produce waves which would roar across the continents, washing away towns as rapidly as the incoming tide will demolish a sand-castle on the beach.

Various calculations have been made. For example, a 50,000,000-ton missile, landing at 10 miles per second, would send a cloud of debris up to over 20 miles, spreading out over at least 150 miles in only 60 seconds. Icarus, which in size and mass is fairly typical of a maverick asteroid, 'weighs' much more than that. So if the Earth were threatened in such a way, it is worth while to decide whether anything could be done about it.

During the last Icarus approach, calculations were actually made by a group working at the Massachusetts Institute of Technology in the United States. They assumed that there would be several weeks' warning, so that there would be enough time – just! – to take action. Various alternatives were proposed. It might be possible to land a nuclear missile on Icarus' surface and then explode it, thereby changing the orbit and diverting it from a collision course. Or the explosion might take place very close to Icarus, with the same result. Perhaps the asteroid might be attacked directly with a hydrogen bomb, either destroying it completely or else breaking it up into small pieces which would make no craters comparable with that which Icarus would produce if it landed intact – in which case the crater diameter would be of the order of 15 miles.

This is all very well, but could we be sure that there would be ample warning? Mrs Helin discovered 1982 DB after it had crossed the Earth's orbit, and even then it was extremely faint, so that an approaching Apollo asteroid could only too easily be missed.

To be honest, there is a near-certainty that some sort of collision will occur every now and then. Asteroids are found in many regions of the Solar System; there are even the so-called Trojans, which move in the same orbit as mighty Jupiter, though they keep prudently out of harm's way and are in no danger of being swallowed up. And in 1977 Charles Kowal, at Palomar in California, discovered a peculiar object which he has named Chiron, which is still further away and spends most of its time between the orbits of Saturn and Uranus. Admittedly Chiron and the known Trojans are relatively large, but what about Hidalgo, whose very elliptical orbit takes it from the inner Solar System out to the neighbourhood of Saturn? Here we have another small body, quite possibly a dead cometary nucleus, and no doubt there are many more of its kind. Over geological ages, the Earth cannot have escaped completely, and it is well worth while casting around to see whether we can find any positive evidence. This brings me on at once to the problem of those remarkable creatures, the dinosaurs.

As most people know, dinosaurs ruled the world for well over 100,000,000 years. Some of them were harmless, while others, such as the tyrannosaurus and allosaurus, were anything but friendly; their huge bodies and their immense teeth would make them ferocious enemies, and while they held sway it was difficult for the smaller, less belligerent mammals to develop. Then, at the end of the geological Cretaceous Period, about 65,000,000 years ago, the dinosaurs disappeared. It was not a gradual process; by cosmical standards it was extremely abrupt, and the end of the dinosaurs was also accompanied by the extinction of many other families of living things, both animals and plants. Something unusual happened, and the puzzle of the death of the dinosaurs is one of the most fascinating in science.

It has been suggested that at the end of the Cretaceous Period, the Earth was bombarded by deadly short-wave radiation from an exploding star or supernova; alternatively that the Sun cooled down for a few million years, so that the Earth's temperature dropped and the vast, unintelligent dinosaurs were unable to adapt. But in recent years the sudden extinction of so many living things has been linked with a possible asteroid collision, an idea supported by both Sir Fred Hoyle and by Clube and Napier. Let me stress at once that we are now considering proposals by eminent and highly respected scientists. The theories may be unconventional, but they must be taken very seriously indeed.

Hoyle begins by working out the probable frequency of impacts by Apollo-type asteroids. He comes to the conclusion that we may expect one hit every 250,000 years or so, but it is clear that the impact at the end of the Cretaceous was exceptional; it is worth bearing in mind that the largest known Apollo asteroid, Hephaistos, is a full six miles in diameter. One effect of the impact, says Hoyle, was to hurl vast quantities of material high above the ground. These particles were reflective, so that for a period of at least 10 years the Earth's upper air reflected back much of the radiation received from the Sun instead of allowing it to pass through to the ground. For a decade, then, the Sun's life-giving warmth was partly cut off. The oceans cooled dramatically; there were constant storms of freezing rain, and the light-level too was reduced. The dinosaurs, unable to see properly in the gloom, found that their food supplies were fatally depleted, and so they died out. The world had entered an ice age, and by the time that conditions reverted to normal the dinosaurs were no more. Hoyle's calculations indicate that at least 50,000 million tons of debris must have been hurled into the upper atmosphere, so that the onset of the Ice Age was remarkably quick.

If this is valid, then another impact might cause a sudden ice age at any time. Hoyle's safeguard is to build vast pumps to stir up the waters of the oceans, bringing up the lower, very cold water to the surface and mixing it so as to prevent a sudden general cooling in the event of another Cretaceous-type strike. It would be necessary only to keep the oceans reasonably warm for a few years; this would be enough. Hoyle also maintains that such a project is well within our capabilities even at the present time, and, to quote his own words:

> The risk of an ice age is not just one of the biggest of the risks that we run. It is a risk that would hopelessly compromise our future. Besides wiping out a considerable fraction of those now alive, it would leave a wan, grey future from which the survivors and their descendants could do nothing to escape. It would be a condition which might last 50,000 years or more, a future in which the prospects for mankind would be much less favourable than they are today. This is why our modern generation must take action to avoid catastrophe, an ultimate catastrophe besides which the problems that concern people, media and governments today are quite trivial.

But would an impact of this kind trigger off an ice age, or would it have precisely the opposite effect? And, for that matter, can we possibly obtain proof that a major impact did occur 65,000,000 years ago?

Some very significant results have been announced by Kenneth Hsü and his colleagues at the Swiss Federal Institute of Technology, who have given what they believed to be reliable confirmation of a Cretaceous strike, but reach results rather different from Hoyle's. They have been studying the sediments from the ocean floor off the coast of Southern Africa, and have found that between the layers laid down in the Cretaceous Period and its successor, the Eocene (by which time the dinosaurs had vanished), there are relatively high concentrations of the element iridium, which is known to exist in meteorites and presumably in asteroids as well. In this particular region there is also a relative lack of chalky material. Now, marine organisms use chalk (calcium carbonate) to build up their shells. Hsü believes that the impact caused a change in the composition of the surface waters; many families or organisms died, while the dust-cloud sent up by the collision blotted out the Sun and stopped plant growth to a large extent. Plants remove carbon dioxide from the atmosphere, by the process of photosynthesis, replacing it with

ABOVE: Dr Velikovsky's theory: the Earth is shown to the lower left. Jupiter (upper right) has emitted the comet Venus (centre right) which has bypassed Mars (lower right) and has lost its tail, thereby being converted into a planet!

BELOW: The Perseid meteors, radiating from a set area of the sky to produce an annual display of cosmic fireworks. Note the Demon Star, Algol, and the brilliant Capella.

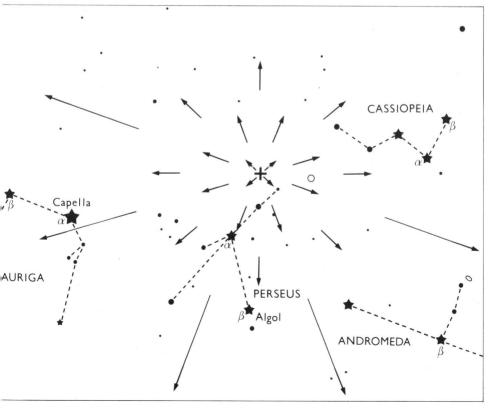

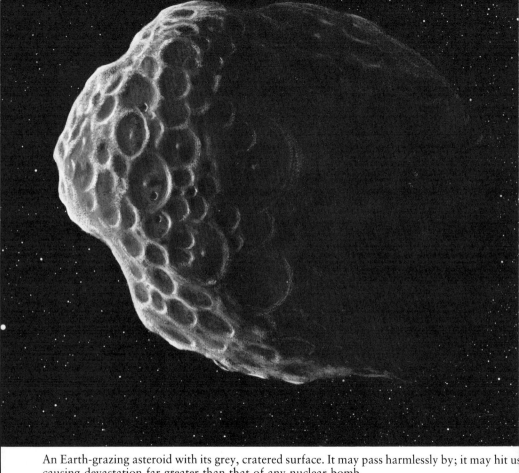

An Earth-grazing asteroid with its grey, cratered surface. It may pass harmlessly by; it may hit us causing devastation far greater than that of any nuclear bomb.

oxygen, so that when this process was halted the amount of carbon dioxide in the atmosphere increased. Since carbon dioxide acts in the manner of a greenhouse, shutting in the Sun's heat, the temperature rose, and the increased heat killed off the dinosaurs and many other living things as well. It took at least 50,000 years for conditions to become normal again, by which time the whole scenario of life on Earth had changed. Note that this idea involves an increase in temperature, not a Hoyle-type ice age, but here too a direct hit from an exceptionally large Apollo asteroid is assumed to be the basic cause.

An increase in the proportion of iridium between the Cretaceous and Eocene layers has been confirmed by other investigators, and it is certainly hard to explain in any theory other than that of an impact. Clube and Napier go further, and link other collisions with mass extinctions of living things further back in Earth history; during the Permian Period (230,000,000 years ago), the Devonian (335,000,000 years) and the Ordovician (435,000,000 years). They also associate asteroid impacts with variations in the Earth's magnetic field.

The Earth acts as a huge magnet. At present the compass needle points to magnetic north (not the same as geographical north, but reasonably close to it), but there are indications that in the distant past the field was reversed, so that a compass needle would point south – as would be the case today on Jupiter, whose magnetic field is admittedly far stronger than ours. The origin of the Earth's magnetic field is still rather uncertain, but is presumably connected with movements in the liquid, iron-rich core, since iron is a magnetic material. A sudden violent impact could cause such global disturbance that the entire magnetic field might be upset, even disappearing completely before things became stable once more and the field returned – quite possibly in the opposite sense. And if there have been times when the Earth had no magnetic field, the surface would have been left unprotected from various harmful radiations coming from space, with disastrous results to living organisms.

However, widespread damage is not the same as the total destruction of the world, and so far as we can tell the Apollo asteroids, whether or not they are ex-comets, are of insufficient mass, while the larger asteroids are in perfectly stable paths well away from us. There is always the chance that the Sun might collect a wandering body large enough to shatter the world if it happened to score a bull's-eye, but the danger is slight. The Earth is over 4,500 million years old; it is roughly half-way through its life-story, and no such disaster has happened yet. In the future we must expect impacts from Apollo-type asteroids, but there is every reason to be confident that even in such a case we would be able to cope with the emergency much better than the dinosaurs did.

Chapter Seven

Star-Crash!

So far we have been discussing possible collisions with members of the Solar System; comets, asteroids or meteorites. But the Solar System is only a very small part of the Galaxy, and we must next turn to the awesome picture of an encounter with a wandering star.

If you take a pair of binoculars or a small telescope and look up at the Milky Way, you will see that it is made up entirely of stars. There are so many that to count them would be quite impossible, and to the unwary observer they seem so close together that they must surely be in imminent danger of bumping into each other. Outwardly, the Milky Way gives the impression of being a very crowded place indeed. Therefore, is our Sun in any danger of being hit by one of its stellar neighbours, with the inevitable destruction of the Earth?

The answer is almost certainly 'no', as astronomers realized as soon as they were able to draw up a reasonable picture of the Galaxy. The first man to do so on really scientific grounds was William Herschel, who came to England from his native Hanover when still a young man, and became a professional organist. In his spare time he made telescope mirrors, and began to study the skies. He achieved fame in 1781, when he happened upon a new planet, the one we now call Uranus (you may recall that it fitted in neatly with Bode's Law), after which King George III gave him a modest pension, and Herschel became a full-time astronomer. He was undoubtedly one of the best and most enthusiastic observers of all time, though admittedly some of his ideas were odd. He even believed that there were intelligent beings living in a cool zone below the bright surface of the Sun.

Herschel set out to discover the shape of the Galaxy, and he decided to use the method of 'star-counts'. He could not hope to count every star visible in his telescopes, since this would have taken him a good many centuries; therefore he selected certain areas, and made 'star-counts' in them. Eventually he came to the conclusion that the Galaxy must be shaped like a 'cloven grindstone', which was not very wide of the mark even though he was wrong in assuming that the Sun, with the Earth, lay near the centre. We now know that the Galaxy is a flattened system with a central bulge, so that I have unromantically compared its shape with that of two fried eggs clapped together back to back. The yolk of the eggs corresponds to the galactic nucleus, which we can never actually see because there is too much interstellar dust in the way. The Sun, plus its planets, lies well out from the nucleus towards the edge, not far from the main plane. The overall diameter of the Galaxy is of the order of 100,000 light-years; the Sun is slightly over 30,000 light-years from the centre of the Galaxy. (Remember that one light-year is equal to 5,880,000,000,000 or somewhat less than six million million miles.)

Seen 'from above' or 'from below', the Galaxy would show spiral arms, like a Catherine-wheel. But from our vantage point the spiral structure is not evident. If we look along the main plane, we see many stars in roughly the same line of sight, i.e. almost one behind the other. This is the cause of the Milky Way band; the stars in it are not genuinely crowded together. There is no three-dimensional effect in space, and appearances can be highly deceptive.

Consequently, we cannot gaze at the Milky Way in the expectation of seeing two stars crash into each other and flare up in protest. Collisions must be very rare indeed, and it is very likely that a star such as the Sun can go right through its life-cycle without experiencing even a near miss. We live in a fairly typical part of the Galaxy, just outside one of the spiral arms, and, as we have seen, the nearest star beyond the Sun is the dim red dwarf, Proxima Centauri, which belongs to the system of Alpha Centauri, one of the pointers to the Southern Cross and therefore too far south in the sky to be seen from Europe or most of the United States. Proxima is 4.2 light-years away, while Alpha Centauri itself is 0.1 of a light-year further out.

Now, 4.2 light-years corresponds to approximately 25 million million miles, and we are virtually certain that there are no stars closer than this; they would have been found by now. Alarms are sounded occasionally, and only a few years ago Olin J. Eggen, working at one of the major observatories in Australia, identified what he thought might be an even closer neighbour, but this turned out to be a mistake; Eggen's Star is a long way off, and Proxima remains the record-holder.

If there is no star within four light-years of us, then obviously there is no fear of a collision, at least in the foreseeable future. There are, of course, more densely-populated regions, particularly in the remarkable systems known as globular clusters, which are regular in outline and which are spectacular when viewed through an adequate telescope. The two finest examples, Omega Centauri and 47 Tucanæ, are in the far south of the sky, but northern-hemisphere observers do at least have the great globular cluster in the constellation of Hercules, which is dimly visible with the naked eye as a misty patch if you know just where to look for it.

At the centre of a globular cluster, the average distance between individual stars is only about half a light-year, and any inhabitants of a planet moving round a star in such a region would have a glorious night sky; there would be many stars shining brilliantly enough to cast shadows, and there would be no proper darkness at all. Also, many of the stars would be red, because in the depths of a globular cluster the leading members are of the type known as Red Giants – a point to which I will return in Chapter 9. Against this, a globular-cluster astronomer would probably know very little about what lay beyond, so that his chances of studying the universe as a whole would be considerably less than ours.

Yet even inside a globular cluster, there can be few collisions. Space is very large, and relatively speaking the stars are very small. If you represent the Earth–Sun distance by one inch, the nearest star, Proxima, will be over four *miles* away.

It is relevant here to say a little about an old theory of how the Earth and the other planets were born. According to the 'passing star' hypothesis, proposed at the turn of the century and popularized by Sir James Jeans (whom many people still remember both for his general books and for his radio broadcasts before and during World War II), a wandering star approached the Sun, and pulled off a cigar-shaped strip of material from the solar surface. As the visitor began to recede, the cigar was left whirling round the Sun; it broke up into drops, and each drop turned into a planet. One attractive feature of this scheme was that the largest planets, Jupiter and Saturn, lie where the thickest part of the 'cigar' would have been. When the mathematicians attacked the theory it had to be somewhat modified, and it was even suggested that the passing star struck the Sun a glancing blow. Alas, even this would not do, and it has now been shown that the whole idea is out of court; like so many appealing and plausible theories, it simply does not work. According to modern ideas, the planets were formed from a 'solar nebula' or cloud of material associated with the youthful Sun.

I mention this because if Jeans had been right, then the Sun would have been one of a very few stars to have met with a 'close encounter'. Planet families would have been excessively rare, and ours might have been the only one in the whole of the Galaxy. On the solar-nebula theory, planetary systems are likely to be commonplace, and this has been borne out by some indirect observations, since a few relatively close and lightweight stars seem to be 'wobbling' as though being pulled upon by invisible bodies of planetary size. Barnard's Star, six light-years away and our closest neighbour beyond the Alpha Centauri group, is one of these.

The Galaxy is rotating, and the Sun takes about 225,000,000 years to complete one journey round the centre. This is sometimes termed the 'cosmic year'. One cosmic year ago, the Earth was in a primitive state; the most advanced life-forms were amphibians, the ancestors of today's frogs and toads, while even the dinosaurs had yet to make their entry. Other stars share in the rotation, but there are some which travel in different paths, and I suppose that we cannot entirely rule out the chance of a collision at some time or other. It is excessively improbable, but it is not impossible. What we can say, with confidence, is that it will not happen yet.

We would have plenty of warning. The first indication would be the movement of one particular star in the sky relative to its background, showing that it must be unusually close. Over the years, or over the centuries, it would brighten up very gradually, until it became prominent enough to be visible with the naked eye. No doubt every Government would do its best to hide the truth because of a fear of mass panic, but eventually it would leak out, and you can well imagine the frantic preparations, though it is not easy to see what could be done without mass emigration to another world – and which world? The whole of the Solar System would be disrupted. Decades more, and the unwelcome newcomer would start to dominate the night sky; then, comparatively quickly, it would become visible in the day-time as well, shining down menacingly as it swooped inwards. At last it would cross the orbits of the outermost planets, and would sear and destroy any which were unfortunate enough to be in the danger-zone. Coming closer and closer, it would perturb the orbit of the Earth; now there would be two suns instead of one, and the whole climate would alter, both because of the extra heat and because of the orbital change. Huge tidal waves would sweep across the continents; if the temperature were raised sufficiently the atmosphere would be driven off, and violent earthquakes would begin, so that the world would revert to its Pre-Cambrian state, when it had still not cooled down sufficiently for life to appear. A direct collision between the Sun and the star would cause an outburst so tremendous that all the inner planets, at least, would be vapourized. Even if there were no actual contact, the star would recede once more leaving behind it a wounded Sun and the ruined remnants of a planet family.

However, it does not seem likely that the Sun will encounter a wandering star during the 5,000 or 6,000 million years left to it before it changes its structure drastically enough to destroy the Earth without any outside help. There is no stellar candidate on view at the moment, so that at the very worst we have many thousands of years' grace!

There is one other possibility. I have been talking about normal stars, shining in much the same way as the Sun, but stars do not last for ever, and eventually they die. The Sun itself will pass through various stages of senility, but it seems certain to end up as a dead, dark globe – in fact, a Black Dwarf. Other stars will meet with a similar fate. Whether the universe has existed for long enough to allow many stars to reach the Black Dwarf condition is questionable, but there ought to be some, and of course they would be extremely hard to detect, because they would send out no radiation at all. We must consider the chances of a meeting with a dead star of this kind.

There is no positive proof that our part of the Galaxy is lacking in Black Dwarfs, and there is even a recent theory which suggests that there may be one in the Solar System itself. The idea is highly speculative, but it is certainly worth looking at rather more closely, which means delving back into history.

All the planets out as far as Saturn were known in ancient times, and they could hardly have been overlooked, because they are prominent naked-eye objects (even Mercury can be quite conspicuous when best placed). As we have seen, Uranus was discovered by Herschel in 1781. He was not looking for a new planet, and did not even recognize it when he found it; he mistook it for a comet, but it would be rather unfair to dismiss his discovery as sheer chance. He was carrying out a systematic review of the sky, and, as he said, if he had missed Uranus on one night he 'must have found it the next'.

Irregularities in the movements of Uranus led to the tracking down of Neptune. Much later, Percival Lowell, the American astronomer who is best remembered today for his admittedly wild theories about intelligent Martians, made calculations of the same sort. He believed in a tenth planet, and in 1930, Clyde Tombaugh, at Lowell's observatory, discovered Pluto not far from the calculated position. Unfortunately, it soon became clear that things were not so satisfactory as had been hoped, because Pluto has proved to be smaller than our Moon and to be made up chiefly of ice; even together with its satellite, Charon, it is not nearly massive enough to pull giant planets such as Uranus or Neptune out of position by any measurable amount. Either Lowell's successful prediction was pure luck, or else Pluto was not the 'tenth planet' for which he had been looking.

Frankly, I do not believe in the 'luck' theory. It would really be too much of a coincidence. This means that Planet Ten really exists, well out beyond Neptune and Pluto, but since it is bound to be very faint we must have at least a vague idea of its position before starting to hunt.

The irregularities in the movements of Uranus and Neptune are of little help, because they are so slight, but now there is a new way of approaching the problem. We may be able to make use of artificial rocket probes, and there are two such spacecraft, Pioneers 10 and 11, which seem to be ideal for the purpose. I modestly claim to have suggested something of the kind in a paper published as long ago as 1975, though in much less precise form.

Pioneers 10 and 11 were designed to make close-range studies of Jupiter. It was impossible to bring them back to Earth; they would be travelling so fast that they would escape from the Solar System altogether, and they would presumably wander around in interstellar space until they were destroyed by collision with some solid body. Each carried a powerful radio transmitter which would be adequate for maintaining contact well after the main part of the mission was over. (They were also fitted with plaques, just in case they were ever picked up by some alien civilization, the idea being that the pictures on the plaques would give a firm clue to their planet of origin.) Pioneer 10 was launched in 1972, and in December 1973 it duly passed within striking distance of Jupiter, sending back the first really detailed information about that strange and hostile world. After its encounter it continued moving outwards, and by mid-1982 it had reached a position between the orbits of Uranus and Neptune.

Pioneer 11 followed a year later. It encountered Jupiter in December 1974, but its work was not over. It still had some fuel reserve, and so it was given an extra burst of power which swung it back across the Solar System to an encounter with Saturn in 1979. By the summer of 1982 it was moving roughly half-way between the orbits of Saturn and Uranus.

The important fact is that Pioneers 10 and 11 are leaving the Solar System on opposite sides, and we are still in touch with them; we may expect to receive signals until well into the 1990s, by which time even the orbits of Neptune and Pluto will have been left far behind. We know exactly where they are, and how they are moving. Suppose, then, that they start to wander away from their predicted paths? We could use them in much the same way as Lowell had used Uranus and Neptune, and under favourable circumstances the Pioneers could even lead us on to Planet Ten, but there are other intriguing possibilities too.

First, take the case in which one Pioneer wanders off course, but not the other. This would indicate a gravitational pull from an outer planet which could not make itself felt on the opposite side of the Solar System. As I said in my original paper, it would be the longest of long shots, because Planet Ten would have to be in just the right place at just the right time, but it could happen.

Next, suppose both probes started to wander. The chances of there being two suitably-placed outer planets would be negligible, and a more plausible candidate would be a much more massive body at a greater distance – say 50,000 million miles or so. Compared with a distance of this sort, the diameter of the Solar System is small, and the Pioneers could be regarded as being at equal distances from the perturbing body, just as for all practical purposes it is good enough to say that Westminster Bridge and the Houses of Parliament are the same distance from the Statue of Liberty.

The perturbing body would be far too massive to be a planet; and since we cannot see it, we would have to assume that it must be a dead star – a companion of the Sun which had come to the end of its luminous career, and had turned into a Black Dwarf. After all, pairs of physically associated stars are common enough in the Galaxy, and even Alpha Centauri is made up of two components, one rather more luminous than the Sun and the other slightly feebler, moving round their common centre of gravity in a period of 80 years.

Tracking down such an object would be very difficult indeed, but if we could establish its existence we would at least know that Black Dwarfs really exist, and if there is one in the Solar System there could well be others wandering around. Should one of them move in towards the Sun, it would be very dangerous indeed. Even if it avoided a direct collision, its pull would throw the Earth into a new orbit, changing our climate completely and probably making it intolerable. The Earth might survive, but humanity would not.

An even more exotic idea is that the perturbing body might be a Black Hole at a still greater distance, say around 100,000 million miles. A Black Hole is produced by a very old, very massive star which has collapsed, and is now pulling so strongly that not even light can escape from it – and if light cannot do so, then certainly nothing else can, because light is the fastest thing in the universe. The tremendously strong pull can suck in material from outside, and it has been said that a Black Hole is a cosmic cannibal, gobbling up material and removing it from all contact with the rest of space. The Sun itself is not massive enough to create a Black Hole (see Chapter 9), and so if the invisible companion is of this type it must have been produced by a star much more substantial than the Sun.

It is reassuring to note that any Black Hole solar companion must be so far away that we are out of the danger-zone. Since it can produce barely detectable effects in the movements of Uranus and Neptune, it is too remote to threaten the Earth. On the other hand, we cannot rule out the chance that there are wandering, undetectable Black Holes in our region of the Galaxy, and there must be a slight but not zero possibility of disaster on this score.

Come, then, to stars which are millions of millions of miles outside the Solar System. Most of them are stable, and shine unchanged for immense spans of time, but some are highly explosive. Into this class come the novæ and, above all, the supernovæ.

Star-Crash!

Nova means 'new', but a nova is not genuinely a new star at all. What happens is that a formerly very faint star flares up suddenly, becoming hundreds or thousands of times its normal brilliance and remaining prominent for a few weeks or months before fading back to obscurity. Novæ have been seen often enough, and some of them have become spectacular. The nova seen in the constellation of Aquila (the Eagle) in 1918 briefly outshone all the stars in the sky apart from Sirius. The last bright nova flared up in 1975 in Cygnus (the Swan), and became brighter than the Pole Star, though its glory was short-lived, and after a week or so it had become too dim to be seen with the naked eye.*

Novæ were once believed to be due to head-on collisions between two stars, but this cannot be correct; as we have seen, stellar encounters are very rare indeed, and novæ are much too frequent to be collision products. In any case, we have now been able to find out a great deal about them. It seems that a nova is really a two-star or binary system, and that one member of the pair drags material away from the other; eventually the system becomes so unstable that a flare-up results. There are also a few stars which have been known to undergo more than one nova-like outburst, notably the 'Blaze Star', known officially as T Coronæ, which burst forth in 1866 and again in 1946.

A supernova is quite different. Here, a very massive star suddenly 'blows up', and at its peak it may shine as powerfully as at least 15,000,000 Suns put together. It also emits a flood of lethal short-wave radiation which would do the Earth no good at all if we happened to be anywhere near.

Supernovæ are uncommon, and over the past 1,000 years only four have been seen in our Galaxy: in 1006, 1054, 1572 and 1604 – all, to the regret of astronomers, before the invention of the telescope, so that our detailed knowledge comes from supernova

---

* I discovered this star myself. Unfortunately, about 70 people had discovered it before me! It was first seen by Japanese astronomers in the afternoon of the day of its flare-up. When the sky darkened over Europe, many observers noticed it independently. As soon as I saw it I made a routine call to the Royal Greenwich Observatory at Herstmonceux, but the nova was so striking that I guessed that I must have been forestalled – and I was right. It has now become so faint that I can no longer follow it even with the powerful telescope in my own observatory.

outbursts seen in remote galaxies millions of light-years away, many of which have been observed in recent years.

From the vague accounts which have come down to us, the 1006 star, in the southern constellation of Lupus (the Wolf) became almost as bright as the quarter-moon; we know where it was, because we can still detect long-wavelength radio emissions from its site even though the star itself has long since vanished. The 1054 supernova, described by Chinese and Japanese astronomers, flared up in Taurus (the Bull), and has left the patch of expanding gas which we call the Crab Nebula, much too faint to be seen with the naked eye or binoculars, but magnificent when photographed through a powerful telescope. Since then we have had the supernovæ of 1572, in Cassiopeia, and 1604, in the Serpent-bearer. All these old supernovæ are radio sources, and it is fortunate for us that they were so far away. The distance of the Crab Nebula is about 6,000 light-years.

Unquestionably a nearby supernova would threaten all life on Earth, but only very massive stars can explode as supernovæ, and there are no stars of this type within range. For supernova candidates we must look for Red Giant stars, which are well advanced in their life-histories. One of the nearest is Scheat, in Pegasus (the Flying Horse) which is about 200 light-years away and is at least 400 times as luminous as the Sun. Another famous Red Giant is Betelgeux in Orion, at over 500 light-years; here the diameter is of the order of 200,000,000 miles (slightly variable, because Betelgeux, like so many Red Giants, is unstable), and the total luminosity would match 15,000 Suns. If Scheat or Betelgeux 'went supernova' they would indeed be glorious, but they are too remote to be dangerous, and in any case they may not suffer any outburst for millions of years yet.

Actually, the best potential supernova candidate is Eta Carinæ, in the far south of the sky. For a time during the last century it outshone every star in the sky except Sirius; at its peak it seems to have had about 6,000,000 times the luminosity of the Sun. It is exceptionally massive, and is associated with magnificent nebula, or cloud of dust and gas. For a century now it has been invisible with the naked eye, but it is still very powerful, and may indeed have lost none of its total luminosity, because a good deal of its light may be blotted out by interstellar material. There are strong indications that Eta Carinæ is approaching its crisis, and that it may be getting ready to destroy itself in a supernova explosion; certainly it cannot continue shining in its present form for more than a 1,000,000 years or so, which is not long on the astronomical time-scale. However, it too is so remote that it could do no more than provide a superb and fascinating spectacle.

Finally, in our list of possible cosmic disasters, we come to the material spread between the stars. There is much more of this than used to be thought, and it has been suggested that the periodical ice ages have been caused when the Sun enters a 'dusty' region, perhaps in one of the spiral arms of the Galaxy, and has its supply of solar radiation drastically reduced. There have been many science-fiction novels written on this theme, notably Sir Fred Hoyle's *The Black Cloud*, but it does not seem to be a serious threat. More-over, the Sun left the last spiral arm at least 10,000 years ago, and we are not due to enter another in the foreseeable future, though it is fair to say that our knowledge of how spiral arms are formed is still very incomplete.

All in all, it seems that we are in no danger from supernovæ or interstellar clouds. Neither is there much chance of an encounter between the Sun and another star, and at the very worst nothing of the kind can happen for millions of years. Much more probably it will never happen at all, so that there is little chance of the Earth being wiped out by a maverick sun.

Chapter Eight

Ordeal by Flying Saucer

I have never personally been involved in an end-of-the world scare. Discounting the mild alarm caused by Dr John Gribbin's Jupiter Effect, none has occurred in England since I was born, and I doubt whether there will be any in the near future. But I have met several people who have vivid memories of a celebrated American scare which occurred on 31 October 1938, and is in a class of its own.

The whole episode was quite unintentional. The man unwittingly behind it was no less than Orson Welles, then a rising young film and radio director and still, of course, one of the world's leading producers and actors. From New York, he decided to put on a wireless adaptation of *The War of the Worlds* by his near-namesake, H. G. Wells, which had been published long before and had been accepted as a science-fiction classic. To those of you who have not read it, the plot is centred upon an invasion of the Earth by grotesque monsters from Mars, who land in Horsell Common, near Woking in Surrey, and run amok with their fighting machines, heat-rays and other charming devices calculated to do the denizens of Earth no good at all. Resistance is futile, and all seems lost, but Nature comes to the rescue at the eleventh hour; the Martians are destroyed by terrestrial bacteria which are absent on their own planet, and against which they have no protection.

Remember that at that period the idea of intelligent life on Mars had not been definitely ruled out. When *The War of the Worlds* was written, in 1901, Percival Lowell and his followers were giving convincing descriptions of Martian canals which, it was said, had been built by the local residents to form a planet-wide irrigation system on a world desperately short of water. All the ice and snow locked up in the white polar caps was pumped through to the warmer regions which were centres of population, and the blobs or 'oases' where two or more canals intersected were regarded as the equivalents of cities. Lowell did not believe in hostile aliens, and indeed he took care to point out that on a planet such as Mars the inhabitants would have to work together; war, he added, was a childish pastime, and the Martians had presumably progressed far beyond any such thing. But of the habitability of Mars he had no doubt at all, and he went so far as to write: 'That Mars is inhabited by beings of some sort or other is as certain as it is uncertain what those beings may be.'

By 1938 many doubts had been expressed, but there was no final proof that the Martians did not exist; it was not until the Space Age, with the flights of the Mariner and Viking probes, that we found out what Mars is really like – a mountainous, cratered world, with lofty volcanoes and dry riverbeds but, unfortunately, no canals. And this lay decades ahead when Orson Welles planned his broadcast.

In his adaptation of the novel, Welles transferred the scene of action from Woking to the United States, and began by putting out what many listeners took to be an actual news bulletin. The effects were startling. I quote here from the London *Daily Mirror* of the following day, 1 November 1938:

> Millions of Americans are today still suffering from nervous prostration after the panic that swept across the country last night during the broadcast of *The End of the World*, a radio adaptation of H. G. Wells' *War of the Worlds*.
>
> Doctors and chemists are reaping a harvest of dollars; hospitals and doctors' surgeries are thronged with nervous breakdown cases. The sales of nerve tonics have soared upwards.
>
> From all parts of the country come reports of people having arms and legs broken in stampedes during the panic.
>
> Millions of American listeners mistook the Wells fantasy for news, and the war scare spread as the radio told of an invasion from Mars.
>
> Thousands got the news second-hand, and soon reports spread that German troops in powerful 'planes and Zeppelins were landing on U.S. soil.
>
> All over America thousands of listeners ran from their homes into the streets, wrapping damp towels round their heads, screaming for gas-masks, falling on their knees in prayer, or dashing off to the countryside, fainting and screaming.

Today there is an impressive reaction, with doctors and nurses rushing to new cases.

Lawyers also report a great increase in business from listeners who plan to sue the radio company and everyone responsible for the broadcast, although during the broadcast commentators did several times try to make it clear that it was fiction.

Psychologists of Columbia and other universities, exalting last night's madness as the greatest mass panic in world history, are calling on listeners for data.

Many people treated by doctors today were still crying hysterically.

One woman patient in a down-town hospital insisted, 'I know it's true. Hundreds are dead somewhere. Roosevelt himself announced it over the radio. I recognized his voice.'

Some insist they saw planes and robot soldiers land from tubular metal ships and fire death-ray guns. Panic lingered longest in Harlem, New York's negro section, where hundreds prayed nearly all night in the streets. Hundreds fought their way into Father Divine's famous temple 'to see the end of the world come'.

Others barricaded themselves in their homes, even blocking windows with furniture 'to keep out the men from Mars'.

At Concorde, Washington, just as the broadcast was announcing that 'monsters were flocking down on United States soil', the lights went out in most of the homes due to a failure in the power.

Terrified inhabitants thought the 'invasion' had reached Washington State, and the town for a time verged on mass hysteria. Women fainted, and men prepared to take their families to the mountains . . . .

From the few eye-witness reports that I have had, I feel that the *Mirror* writer may have exaggerated things somewhat, but of the panic itself there was no question. People actually saw the fighting machines, felt the heat-rays and witnessed luckless folk being fried like eggs in the searing blasts. And here, surely, we have a forerunner of the flying saucer or UFO stories that are still with us.

Mars has always been regarded as the planet most likely to harbour intelligent life, and there have been various efforts to establish contact. I particularly like the idea put forward in the

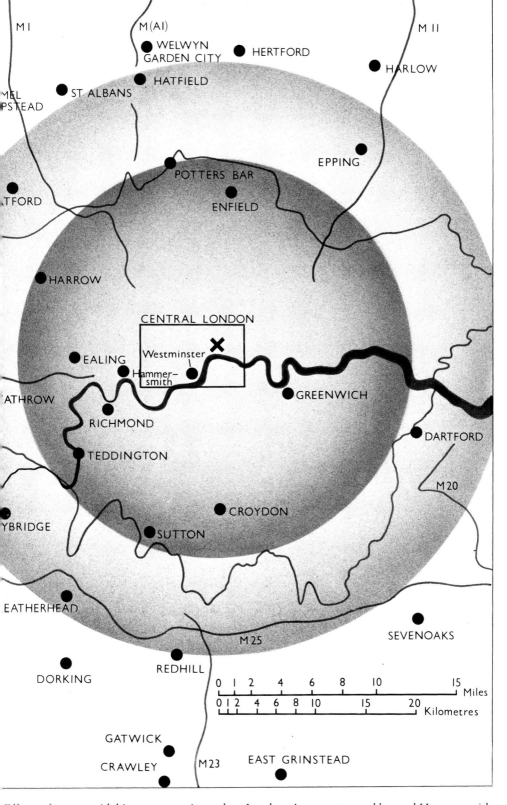

Effects of an asteroidal impact on a city such as London. Areas out to and beyond Hammersmith would be totally destroyed; the damage would extend out to St Albans and Redhill.

Tunguska. The pine trees have stood silently and with dignity for many centuries – until the blazing visitor from outer space crashed down, and laid them flat, scorching them in the process.

A puzzled dinosaur, looking up at a brilliant fireball streaking across the sky and no doubt thinking that such things could never have happened in the Triassic Period!

1870s by a Frenchman named Charles Cros, who wanted to build a huge burning-glass and focus the Sun's rays on to the Martian deserts, swinging the lens around and writing words. I have often wondered what words he meant to write – and what would have been our own reactions if the Martians had responded similarly, so that vast letters had started to appear in the Sahara? There was always the possibility that the Martians would be civilized enough to speak English or some other terrestrial language, but the whole method seemed somewhat cumbersome, and the French Government refused to finance it, so that it was never actually put to the test. At the turn of the century a prize was offered, again in France, to anyone who could get in touch with an extra-terrestrial civilization, but Mars was specifically excluded, because the donors thought that calling up the Martians would be too easy.

Various wireless messages have been sent, and in 1924 the British Post Office went so far as to accept a telegram for a Martian address, charging 1s. 6d. per word but prudently marking it 'Reply not guaranteed'. And in 1939, a year after the Welles scare and at a time when Mars was particularly brilliant, a Surrey radio amateur who rejoiced in the name of A. Bird claimed that he had succeeded in receiving coded signals from the Red Planet, though to the best of my knowledge he never revealed what the Martians had said.

Today we know much more about Mars than we did in the days of Lowell, or even Mr Bird. The breakthrough came in 1965, when the American probe Mariner 4 by-passed the planet and sent back pictures showing craters – which were the last things that most astronomers had expected. In 1971 Mariner 9 was put into a closed orbit around Mars, and we had our first views of the giant volcanoes, one of which – Olympus Mons or Mount Olympus – towers to 15 miles above the general level of the surface, and is crowned by a 40-mile caldera. The climax came in 1976, when two Viking spacecraft made gentle landings, one in the ochre desert of Chryse and the other in the rather inappropriately named Utopia. The scene was one of red, barren rocks under a pink sky; the atmosphere, made up chiefly of the unbreathable gas carbon dioxide, was much thinner than our air at the top of Everest, and was impregnated with fine dust. Samples scooped up from the deserts and analysed inside the probes showed no trace of life, either past or present. We cannot yet be absolutely sure that Mars is sterile, but most astronomers believe so. At the very best we cannot hope to find anything more advanced than lichen or moss, and Lowell's brilliant-brained Martians, with their elaborate canal system and their thriving cities, have been reluctantly banished to the pages of novels. No doubt men from Earth will reach Mars eventually, perhaps within the next 50 years, but they will find no reception committees to greet them, and neither will they be met by wide-eyed demonstrators proclaiming 'Earthmen, go home!'

When we look around the other planets in the Solar System, we are forced to conclude that they make up a decidedly unfriendly collection. Venus, which shines so gloriously in our skies, has a ground temperature of about 900 degrees Fahrenheit, a crushing carbon-dioxide atmosphere, and clouds containing sulphuric acid, so that any astronaut incautious enough to step outside his spacecraft would be at once squashed, poisoned, fried and corroded. Mercury is virtually without atmosphere, and is in many ways not unlike the Moon apart from being considerably hotter during its day-time. The giant planets, Jupiter and the rest, have gaseous surfaces, so that landing there would be somewhat difficult, and in general their satellites are almost as unwelcoming. Probably the most interesting of them is Titan, the senior member of Saturn's numerous satellite family. It is not much smaller than Mercury, and has a dense atmosphere composed mainly of nitrogen, the gas which makes up 78 per cent of the air that you and I are breathing. Organic compounds exist on Titan, and it may be said that there are all the ingredients for life, but there seems no doubt that the extreme cold has prevented any living things from developing. Titan is unique; on its surface there may be cliffs of solid methane, with rivers of liquid methane and a constant rain of methane from the thick clouds. But so far as intelligent life is concerned we can certainly rule it out, and I for one have no faith whatsoever in totally alien beings, such as jellyfish-like creatures swimming in an ocean of liquid hydrogen below the visible surface of Jupiter or Saturn.

Yet . . . what about flying saucers? Do they exist, and if so, do they pose any threat either to mankind or to the Earth itself?

The saucer story began abruptly on 24 June 1947. A businessman named Kenneth Arnold was flying his private aeroplane over the Cascade Mountains, in Washington State, when he saw nine circular objects in obvious formation, moving at a high speed and passing him at a distance which he estimated as 25 miles (though I am not clear as to how he arrived at this figure). He wrote: 'They flew like a saucer would if you skipped it across the water' – and the term Flying Saucer was born.

Other reports, even more sensational, started to come in thick and fast, but the real crunch dated from 1953, with the publication of the classic *Flying Saucers Have Landed*, written jointly by George Adamski and Desmond Leslie. I knew Adamski (who died some years ago) and I still know Desmond, so that I have had first-hand accounts. Adamski, so we learn, actually encountered a grounded saucer when he was driving along near the Californian coast; he established that it came from Venus, and he talked to the crew members, though at that time they did not speak English, and sign-language had to be used. Subsequently, as he related in later books, he went for several enjoyable trips, and met not only Venusians but also Martians and Saturnians – all of whom had by this time decided to speak excellent broken American, which made things a great deal easier.

Next on the scene was Cedric Allingham, an amateur bird-watcher who, so he told me (and as he wrote in his book) met a Martian on the Scottish coast, and even photographed him, thereby establishing that the Martians, like ourselves, wear braces to keep their trousers up.

Throughout the 1950s, flying-saucer stories increased daily; societies were founded, and what had begun as something of a joke turned rapidly into a cult which was taken quite seriously. Even the United States Air Force became interested, and set up an organization to try to decide whether the stories had any basis of reality. Gradually, too, the term, flying saucer, was dropped, to be replaced by the more dignified Unidentified Flying Object, or UFO for short. Not everyone was impressed, and it is on record that Andrei Gromyko, then Russian Foreign Minister, suggested that the saucers were due to a Soviet discus thrower who had been practising for the Olympic Games and had failed to appreciate his true strength. Nevertheless, UFOs had come to stay, for a while at least, and before long there were suggestions that they might be hostile.

Let me make one point clear. You may or may not believe that people such as George Adamski and Cedric Allingham have met beings from other worlds; I admit that I do not, but I do not doubt the sincerity of the reports, and most of what has been said and written is completely harmless. There is nothing objectionable about George going on a trip round the Moon, or Cedric helping his Martian colleague to adjust his braces. But spreading alarm and despondency is another matter, and some UFO authors have been guilty of it. There was even a mild panic, confined to the State of Michigan and initiated by a college lecturer, Dr Charles Laughead, who claimed to have been in touch with a mystic and had been converted. There would be floods and earthquakes following a new visitation by UFOs, and only those who were true Believers would be saved from a watery grave. Dr Laughead gave the fateful day as 21 December 1954, and a crowd of people gathered near his home, only mildly reassured by the news that a UFO would land and pick them up from the good doctor's back garden. By that time Laughead had been dismissed from the State College, but even after 21 December had passed without incident he remained convinced that the messages had been genuine; God had intervened to stop the flood at the last moment.

I have no knowledge of any further alarms of the same type, but by now there are many books which claim that the visiting aliens are far from benign. The oddest theory of all is that the UFOs come from inside the hollow Earth, and emerge through a hole at the North Pole; apparently the underground races are preparing to take us over – one method being to dump pumas in the countryside to act as scouts and report back to their masters, so that if you hear mewing sounds from beneath your feet you will know that a new spy is about to be dispatched. In London, the House of Lords held a solemn debate about the whole UFO problem, thereby proving that W. S. Gilbert was on the right track when he wrote *Iolanthe*.

Then there are cases of people who have mysteriously disappeared, and have, it is claimed, been snatched up in spacecraft. The aircraft crashes over what has become known as the Bermuda Triangle are also mentioned, though cynical ex-flyers such as myself suspect that the accidents have been due merely to poor conditions of visibility or to human error. Neither must we forget the books by Erich von Däniken, who maintains that the Earth was visited in ancient times, and that God himself may well have been an astronaut. Moreover, what about the Aetherius Society?

. I do not propose to say much about them here, because I have done so elsewhere,* but I cannot avoid mentioning them, because if

---

*In my book *Can You Speak Venusian?*, published in its revised edition in 1977.

their statements are correct they have on several occasions helped to prevent the world from being destroyed. They have been able to do this because their Founder/President, formerly Mr George King of the Fulham Road, London, and now the Rev. Dr Sir George King of California, is on first-name terms with several important person-ages, including Aetherius, who lives on Venus but who looks after the Earth; Jesus Christ, who is based on Mars; and Confucius, who has been transferred to Saturn, the most advanced of the planets and also the seat of the Interplanetary Parliament. During one crisis, of which most people (including myself) were blissfully unaware, hostile fishmen from across the Galaxy launched a missile towards us, mainly because the oceans on their own world were drying up and they wanted to make use of ours. The news of the impending attack percolated through to the Interplanetary Parliament, which decided to take action. Aetherius was away at the time, but Dr King was informed, and eventually a Martian-launched thunderbolt blasted the missile out of the sky before it could reach us. Now and then, it is important to organize Spiritual Pushes, and also to charge the tops of mountains with Cosmic Energy to make sure that no unfriendly aliens can penetrate our defences. Most of the UFOs, which may be up to 5,000 miles long, come from either Mars or Venus, while Jupiter is the reception planet of the Solar System, and visitors from outer space have to have their passports stamped there before travelling on. Circling the Earth there are several space stations, including Mars Sector 6, which Dr King has actually visited in his capacity as our representative to the Interplanetary Parliament . . .

At least it is comforting to know that we are being so well guarded, and that future onslaughts by the fishmen are likely to be as unproductive as the first. But all in all, what are the chances of global destruction by alien attack?

Of course the idea is very old, and many stories have been written on the theme, notably Wells' *War of the Worlds*. And though we can expect no advanced life-forms in the Solar System, except on Earth, it would be both vain and illogical to claim that we are alone in the universe. The Sun is one of a 100,000 million stars in our Galaxy, and our telescopes are capable of photographing at least 1,000 million galaxies, so that the total number of stars is beyond our comprehension. If planetary systems are common, as seems to be indicated by modern theory, we may expect many Earth-like planets orbiting Sun-like stars. Consider, for instance, the southern star Delta Pavonis, which is easily visible with the naked eye, though it is too far south to be seen from Europe. It is 19 light-years away, and almost identical with our Sun. There is no reason why it should not be attended by an equivalent of the Earth, and Delta Pavonis is a very run-of-the-mill star. If conditions there are much the same as here, similar life-forms could well have appeared.

I realize that this view is open to challenge, and that at least one of the world's most eminent astronomers is of the opinion that we are unique. Yet every time we have tried to set ourselves upon a pinnacle, we have been disillusioned. Originally it was believed that the Earth was flat, lying at rest in the centre of the universe. Then, when the Greeks showed that the world is a globe, it was still assumed to retain the central position (though a few thinkers, such as Aristarchus of Samos, disagreed). After the revolution in outlook sparked off by Copernicus in the 16th century and concluded by Newton with the publication of his *Principia* in 1687, it was still maintained that the Sun at least was of real importance. Next, the Sun was shown to be a normal dwarf star, and finally, in our own century, came the revelation that our Milky Way galaxy is a normal star system. Today it is even suspected that there are super-clusters of galaxies, and that we may be seeing only a fraction of the universe.

Not to put too fine a point on it, we have been taken down not merely one peg, but a great many pegs, and if life appears wherever conditions are suited to it we may assume that intelligent beings are scattered throughout our Galaxy and others. They might not look in the least like us, and I am quite prepared to believe in intelligent astronomers with, say, three legs each and several arms, but they would not truly be what science-fiction writers usually term BEMs or Bug-Eyed Monsters. So far as we can tell, all the material in the universe is made up of the same elements as those we know. When we use spectroscopes to analyse the light coming from remote stars or remote galaxies, we find the familiar substances: hydrogen, carbon, iron and the rest. There is no reason to suppose that other elements exist, and every reason to suppose that they do not. This means that all life-forms, wherever they are found, are built up in essentially the same way as ourselves.

I may be wrong. It is not impossible that there is a fundamental flaw in this reasoning, and that the truth is much more complicated. But when you are presented with a set of facts which is admittedly incomplete, the only course is to interpret them as sensibly as you can. Unless any contrary evidence turns up, it is reasonable to believe that extra-terrestrial life will be of our own type, and that we will find no beings made of pure gold living in airless worlds.

Whether our own natures are typical, I do not know. Frankly I hope not, because we have little reason to be proud of ourselves, as two world wars within living memory have shown. I will return to this theme later. Meanwhile, let us remember that civilization as we know it is very young. Ten thousand years ago the world was emerging from its latest Ice Age, and a visiting astronaut would have found very little in the way of technology. A million years ago, any alien who landed on Earth would have discovered no 'intelligence' at all by modern standards. Yet a million years is not long when we recall that the world is well over 4,000 million years old, so that civilization as we know it has developed in an amazingly short period of time. Mechanical transport would have seemed far-fetched to Julius Cæsar or King Canute, and the idea of travelling to the Moon would have been dismissed out of hand. Unfortunately our science has far outstripped our ethics, and I would not claim that in this sense we have made any progress since the time of Ancient Athens.

The situation has altered dramatically over the past few decades. Before 1945, battles were fought mainly between professional armies, and though many innocent people were killed the result did not matter fundamentally in the long run. Rome destroyed Carthage, and drove a plough over its site; if Carthage had destroyed Rome instead, I would still be seated at my desk typing the manuscript of this book. But when the first atom bomb exploded over Hiroshima, the danger spread to the whole of *homo sapiens*. We know, with uneasy certainty, that we have the capacity to wipe ourselves out.

Therefore, we are in the midst of our greatest crisis. We are technologically advanced, but we are still primitive in our outlook. If we manage to avoid self-destruction for another couple of centuries, we may well learn enough to control our savage instincts; time will tell. It could be that every civilization, wherever it arises, undergoes the same test. If so, then there must be worlds which are still in what may be called the caveman state; worlds where the inhabitants are in the same stage of evolution as ourselves; worlds where civilization has flowered, and where true enlightenment has succeeded mental darkness. There must also, I fear, be worlds which are lifeless and radioactive, and which have been rendered permanently uninhabitable.

This is not really a digression, because we are considering the possibility of invasion by an alien race. Certainly we are not yet in a position to attempt direct contact with another planetary system. Rockets would take an impossibly long time to reach even the nearest star; if we are to get in touch with far-away races, we must await some fundamental breakthrough about which we cannot speculate as yet, because we have not the faintest notion where to start. Methods such as teleportation and thought-travel are as far-fetched to us as television would have been 1,000 years ago.

Now let me come to the real crux of my argument. Any civilization which has learned how to cross interstellar space, either materially or (more probably) by some other means, must have passed through its crisis period and survived. If it had remained warlike, as we are at the moment, it would have liquidated itself. Consequently, any visitors from outer space will not be hostile, and we will have nothing to fear from them. I cannot agree with those scientists who have publicly proclaimed that to send out radio messages, advertising our presence, is to court disaster. It is always possible that an unfriendly civilization might pick up our transmissions and even interpret them, but this could do no harm. Other beings could reach us only if they were genuinely enlightened, and in such a case we could learn a great deal from them.

There is no proof that aliens have ever visited us; the 'evidence' put forward by Erich von Däniken and others does not stand up to examination, and is really no more credible than George Adamski's Venusians or Mr King's Interplanetary Parliament. Yet a visitation is not out of the question, and one day it may come. Following the same argument, other races will have no cause to fear us if we ourselves master the secret of interstellar flight, because we will then have progressed far beyond our present dangerous state of mind.

In short, it seems there is no chance that the world will end because of alien attack. There is therefore no need to be alarmed on that score.

Efforts have already been made to pick up signals from far-away civilizations, but it is hardly surprising that so far these experiments have met with no success. Meanwhile, our first messengers to outer space are already on their way. The Pioneers, as we have seen, carry plaques. The Voyagers, which also will leave the Solar System permanently, do more; they carry records of sounds ranging from the voice of the Secretary-General of the United Nations through to barking dogs, crying babies and pop music. I can well imagine the feelings of an Alpha Centaurian who opens the capsule, puts the record on a turntable, and listens. Once he hears the pop music, he may easily, and justifiably, decide to leave us well alone!

Chapter Nine
And So to Science

Up to now we have been discussing ways in which the world will *not* end. Religion gives no clue; the gravitational pulls of the planets, even when working in unison, cannot affect us; the Moon is set firmly and comfortingly in its orbit; we are unlikely to be hit by a major asteroid or a wandering comet; the stars are too remote to threaten us, and we are in no danger from alien beings or flying saucers. It might be thought, then, that I am setting out to prove that the world is eternal. Not so! It has a limited life-span ahead of it, so let us now turn to what sober science can tell us.

The most important factor of all is the Sun, which sends us virtually all our light and heat. Without the Sun, our Earth would never have come into existence, and we are entirely dependent upon it; if its luminosity changed by even a few per cent, the results so far as we are concerned would be disastrous. Therefore we have to decide whether the Sun's output is likely to alter in the foreseeable future, and this involves saying something about stellar evolution.

It is fairly certain that the Sun, like all other stars, condensed out of interstellar material contained in a nebula. Nebulæ, made up of dust and gas, are common enough; the Great Nebula in Orion, near the Hunter's Belt, is a superb example, and any small telescope will show it well, together with four hot stars in the so-called 'Trapezium' which make the nebula shine. (Were there no suitable stars, the nebulosity would be dark, and would be detectable only by the fact that it would blot out the light of stars beyond. Dark nebulæ are also common; look for instance at the 'Coal Sack' in the Southern Cross, or the dark rifts in the Milky Way running through Cygnus, the Swan.) The Orion Nebula is a stellar birthplace. It is over 1,000 light-years away, and is of tremendous extent, though the gas in it, mainly hydrogen, is millions of times less dense than the

Earth's air. Fresh stars are being produced in the Nebula, and at least two have been caught in the act, since they started to shine only a few decades ago. There are also many stars in the Nebula which are very young and are unstable, so that they vary in brilliancy. Rather confusingly these are known as T Tauri stars, because T Tauri itself, in the adjacent constellation of the Bull, was the first-discovered member of the class. And deep in the Orion Nebula, permanently hidden from us, is the mysterious Becklin-Neugebauer Object, named after its co-discoverers. It may well be a very young, immensely powerful star, detectable only because it sends out floods of infra-red radiations which, unlike visible light, can slice through the nebular dust and gas.

According to modern estimates, the Sun was born rather over 5,000 million years ago – not suddenly, but over a long period. Inside a dusty, hydrogen-rich cloud, a chance condensation formed; as it grew, its gravitational pull drew in extra material, and eventually the embryo star became so hot inside that it started to shine. At first it flickered irregularly, as the T Tauri stars do now, but eventually it steadied. By then the planets had been produced, and among these, of course, were the Earth and Venus.

There was a protracted period when the Sun had only about 70 per cent of its present luminosity. The inner parts of the Solar System were cooler, and since Venus and the Earth are near-twins in size and mass they began to evolve along similar lines. But before long, conditions changed, and the Sun became hotter. Earth, at a respectful 93,000,000 miles, escaped the worst of the blast; Venus did not, and suffered dramatically. The seas boiled and then evaporated; life was extinguished, and as the carbonates in the rocks were driven out Venus developed the thick, carbon-dioxide atmosphere which still acts in the manner of a greenhouse, shutting in the Sun's heat and raising the surface temperature to a furnace-like 900 degrees Fahrenheit or so. If this scenario is correct (and very recent evidence does point that way), then Venus must be regarded as a tragic world, where life had no chance to evolve beyond its primitive state before being ruthlessly snuffed out.

Before going on, let me pause to dispose of another end-of-the-world suggestion, this time involving the giant planet Jupiter.

Jupiter and Saturn are much the largest members of the Sun's family; Jupiter could accommodate over a 1,000 globes the volume of the Earth. Not so very long ago they were believed to be miniature suns. In a famous book, *Saturn and its System*, written by the English astronomer, R. A. Proctor in 1882, we find the following: 'A disturbance in Jupiter, and still more in Saturn, to be recognizable from the Earth, must take place on a scale incomparably greater than that on which any terrestrial disturbances, even the most tremendous earth-throes, have taken place within the knowledge of man. Over a region hundreds of thousands of square miles in extent, the glowing surface of the planet must be torn by subplanetary forces. Vast masses of intensely hot vapour must be poured forth from beneath, and rising to enormous heights, must either sweep away the enwrapping mantle of cloud which had concealed the disturbed surface, or must itself form into a mass of cloud.'

This seemed reasonable enough a century ago, and it was not finally disproved until the 1920s, with a series of brilliant theoretical papers by Sir Harold Jeffreys. Direct measurements showed later that far from being hot, the surfaces of Jupiter and Saturn are extremely cold, so the dwarf-sun theory was ruled out.

Yet inside Saturn, and still more so inside the larger and more massive Jupiter, the temperatures must be high, and the pressures are tremendous. One idea, originating in the Soviet Union, is that Jupiter is still scooping up material from the debris which litters the Solar System, and that its mass is increasing, so that eventually the core will become so hot that nuclear reactions will be triggered off. The planet Jupiter will be transformed into the star Jupiter, and the effects on Earth will be dire. Life will probably be wiped out, and the gravitational disturbances might even suck our hapless world into one of the two suns.

This sounds alarming, but in fact it is absolutely out of the question. For one thing, the amount of fresh material which Jupiter could collect is neglible when compared with the present mass of the planet. Though the present core temperature may be as much as 30,000 degrees Fahrenheit, this is very low as against the critical value of 10,000,000 degrees which would be needed to make the change from planet into star.

In some respects the Sun itself must be regarded as variable, because of the famous 11-year cycle. The bright solar surface or photosphere, at a temperature of almost 6,000 degrees Centigrade, is not blank; on it may be seen darker patches known, rather misleadingly, as sunspots. They are not truly dark, but appear so by contrast with the still brighter background, and they change constantly, so that they are fascinating to watch.* They are not always present; no individual spot or spot-group lasts for more than a few months at most, and smaller spots are often gone in a matter of days or even hours. At times of solar maximum (as in 1957–8, 1968–9 and 1979–80) there are many spot-groups, together with flares – violent outbursts which emit streams of electrified particles which cross the 93,000,000-mile gap to Earth and cascade down into the atmosphere, producing the lovely displays of auroræ or polar lights – whereas at times of minimum there may be many consecutive spotless days. The cycle is by no means perfectly regular, but we may expect the next maximum around 1991.

It used to be thought that there was a definite link between the solar cycle and our weather. Nowadays the association is generally regarded as dubious, but it is certainly worth looking back to see if we can find any longer-term cycles. Records indicate that between 1645 and 1715 there were practically no sunspots at all, so that the cycle was suspended; this is known as the Maunder Minimum, after the English astronomer who drew attention to it 90 years ago. This protracted minimum coincided with what is often termed 'the little ice age', when the Thames froze over frequently, and the climate in Iceland was so severe that there was talk of evacuating the whole island. Similar spotless periods seem to have occurred earlier, though we cannot be nearly so confident about them because the records are fragmentary.

There is another interesting fact, too. Theory shows that the Sun ought to emit many of the particles known as neutrinos, which are difficult to study because they have no electrical charge and almost (or quite) zero mass. Experiments indicate that the total neutrino flux is much less than theory expects, so that either our knowledge of the Sun's interior is much less than we used to think, or else the Sun really is behaving in an abnormal manner at the present moment.

---

*Let me repeat a warning which I have given before on countless occasions: never look directly at the Sun through any telescope or binoculars, even with the addition of a dark filter. Permanent damage to the eye, or even total blindness, is almost certain to result. To observe sunspots, project the Sun's image through the telescope on to a white screen or card held behind the eyepiece. On no account look direct, even for a moment.

If the Sun's output of radiation fell, then so would the temperature of the Earth, and this brings us back to the whole question of ice ages. Asteroid impacts may have been responsible, but it seems rather more likely that the basic cause is to be found in the fluctuations of the Sun. These may have occurred in the relatively recent past. The last Ice Age ended a mere 10,000 years ago, by which time Man had become firmly established upon the terrestrial scene. Actually, the Ice Age was not a period of constant cold. There were four chilly spells, interspersed with warmer periods which are termed interglacials – and we may even now be in the midst of an interglacial, in which case the true Ice Age may not be over yet. In any event, there is no doubt that for some time prior to 8000 BC the general temperature of the world was appreciably lower than it is now. The ice-caps at the poles were much more extensive, and the northern ice-sheet extended down almost as far as modern London. At that time England was joined on to the mainland, and it would have been possible for an Ice-Age sportsman to skate across from, say, Norfolk to Norway.

We know much less about conditions in the Antarctic, because there are no continents near the south pole apart from Antarctica itself, which is still ice-covered and which has no human population apart from the scientists who work at the various research bases. Otherwise, Antarctica is left to penguins and other amiable creatures, who are not in the least worried about the end of the world or, indeed, about anything except finding enough fish to eat for dinner. But the evidence now indicates that during the Ice Age the south, too, was colder than at present, in which case the drop in temperature affected the whole world. This means that ice ages can hardly have been due to a shift in the direction of the Earth's axis, which was a favoured theory at one time. If the poles shifted, then admittedly some parts of the world would have been chilled, but others would have become correspondingly warmer.

However, there are some people today who are very worried about the possibility of such a shift, and there is a fully-fledged Pole Watchers Society, which is keeping alert for any sign of danger.

As most people know, the present tilt of the Earth's axis is $23\frac{1}{2}$ degrees to the perpendicular of its orbit, which is why we have our seasons; during northern summer the north pole is tipped sunwards, while the south pole is inclined in the opposite direction. The fact that the Earth is actually closest to the Sun in December is more or less irrelevant, because the difference is only about 3,000,000 miles, and the effect is masked by the stabilizing influence of the great southern oceans. To alter the tilt deliberately would be too much for 20th-century technology, even if it were wise. There was a famous story by Jules Verne, *The Purchase of the Pole*, in which some experimenters try to change the tilt by using the recoil of a huge cannon, but fail because a careless professor had been making the essential calculations on a blackboard when he fell off his chair, thereby wiping out a vital string of zeros. But the pole watchers of today treat the whole matter very seriously.

I first came across them in 1954, with the publication of a booklet by Adam D. Barber entitled *Disaster Worse than the H-Bomb*. In fact, he was kind enough to send me a personal copy – though I was not singled out; other recipients were Sir Winston Churchill, General de Gaulle, the President of the United States, the Emperor of Japan, and the Pope. Barber was fascinated by gyroscopes, and in particular by the fact that the Earth is wobbling very slowly in the manner of a gyroscope which is about to topple; we have come across this effect earlier, when discussing the astrologers. Barber came to the eventual conclusion that in addition to its orbit round the Sun, the Earth also describes a 'small orbit', so that when the Earth's axis makes a right angle with both the large and small orbits it is liable to slip suddenly by 135 degrees, making the north pole shift by 90 degrees.

To be candid, I have never been able to follow Barber's reasoning, so let me quote from his book:

'The shift is basically caused by gyroscopic processes at right angles to the two orbits of the Earth. This occurs because the Earth itself is a huge gyroscope, and when it reaches the dead centre of its orbits it can no longer press forward. On account of its momentum in its orbit, it creates a gyroscopic pressure at right angles, thereby causing a sudden shift . . . The shift will be completed in about one and a half hours.'

He went on to say that this shift happens every 9,000 years, the last occasion being (naturally) the time of Noah's Flood, when the seas swept across the lands and produced a global deluge. Finally, he maintained that the danger times were 21 June and 21 December each year, when the Earth 'reaches the extremes of its orbit'.

Barber's book failed to make the impact which he had expected, but, nothing daunted, he continued to make predictions as well as suggest remedies – in particular, fixing powerful jets to the Earth at the two poles, so that firing the motors would stop the shift as soon as it was first noticed! As an extra precaution, he recommended that everyone should build a boat and moor it in a convenient position, so that it could be used immediately the flood-waters arrived. Shades of President Auriol of Toulouse . . . .

In fact there is absolutely no evidence of Barber's 'small orbit', even if you could fathom exactly what it was meant to be, and neither can we have much faith in the theories of another pole-shift enthusiast, Hugh Auchincloss Brown, who died in 1975 at the advanced age of 96. Mr Brown did not believe in Barber-type orbits. Instead, he believed that the weight of the Antarctic ice-cap was increasing so much that it would eventually upset the stability of the entire globe, causing it to topple sideways. In his book *Cataclysms of the Earth*, published in 1967, he forecast that at the next shift New York would be submerged 13 miles below the surface of the ocean. His remedy was to break up the ice-cap with atomic bombs, preventing it from becoming dangerously heavy.

Yet another idea was proposed by Charles Hapgood, of the United States, in 1949. This time only the crust of the Earth would slip, gliding over the molten interior; the movement was likely to be very slow, taking thousands of years, and Mr Hapgood was inclined to think that it had already started, so that violent earthquakes might be expected in the future. I must also mention Richard Kieninger and his followers of the Stelle Group, based 70 miles from Chicago, who adopt a modified version of the Jupiter Effect. They even give a date: 5 May 2000, when, they claim, the planets will line up and cause the Earth to tip. Finally there is, of course, Dr Velikovsky, whose theories embraced almost every version of eccentricity, and who also included pole shifting in several of his books.

It is true that there are modest fluctuations in the inclination of the axis over a cycle of 41,000 years, so that the tilt ranges between $21\frac{1}{2}$ degrees and $24\frac{1}{2}$ degrees, but this is not enough to make a great deal of difference to our climate, and it is certainly too slight and too gradual to worry about. The changes are due to the gravitational pulls of the Sun and Moon, and there is no conceivable mechanism, apart possibly from a really major asteroid collision, which could cause a rapid shift. Incidentally, most of the other planets have axial inclinations much the same as ours, though Jupiter is almost

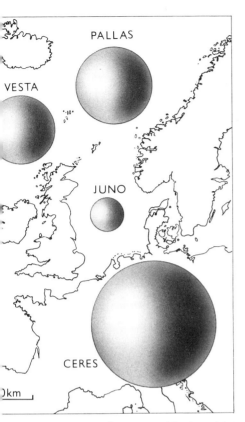

ABOVE LEFT: Asteroids compared in size with Europe. Ceres, with a diameter of over 600 miles is much the largest and most massive of the whole swarm, though Vesta is brighter.

ABOVE RIGHT: The Sun's position in the Galaxy; (top) near the edge of a spiral arm, around 33,000 light-years from the centre and (lower) lying almost in the main plane.

BELOW: The sky from a planet near a globular cluster – a huge system of up to 1,000,000 stars, dominating one part of the sky and creating a brilliant light.

ABOVE: A Black Hole in orbit with a giant star. The Black Hole is pulling material away from the giant; before the material passes over the event horizon of the Black Hole, it is intensely heated and emits X-rays.

BELOW: The Hertzsprung-Russell Diagram, of fundamental importance to all astronomers. The Main Sequence runs from upper left to lower right. The Sun is a typical Main Sequence star.

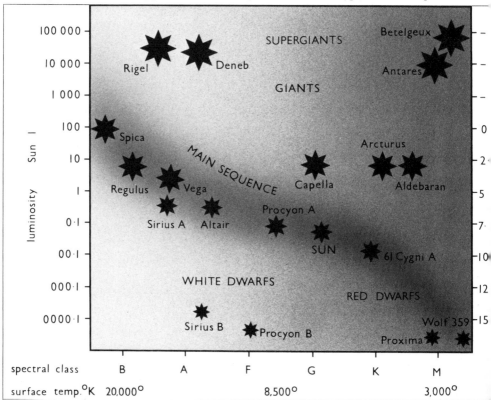

'upright', Venus spins in the opposite sense to the Earth for some unknown reason, and Uranus is tilted over at an angle of 98 degrees, so that there are times when one pole of the planet is turned directly towards the Sun. The Uranian seasons must be most peculiar; each pole would have a night lasting for 21 Earth-years, with a corresponding midnight sun at the opposite pole, though it is hardly likely that there are any inhabitants to study it.

No; all these suggested calamities must be discounted. The real, ultimate peril comes from the Sun.

Since the Sun is so hot, it is tempting to suggest that it is burning, in the manner of a coal fire. The surface temperature is almost 6,000 degrees Centigrade, which is warm by any standards, and the inner temperature is much higher still. Yet the Sun is too hot to burn; and if it were made up entirely of coal, blazing furiously enough to send out as much heat as the real Sun actually does, it would not last for long before being turned into ashes. Unlike the phœnix, it would be unable to recreate itself, and we must look for a different source of energy. Before going any further I must say something about the spectroscope, which is one of the most important of all astronomical instruments and which many people regard as the most vital of all, though admittedly it does have to be used in conjunction with a powerful telescope.

The initial steps were taken by Isaac Newton in 1666, when Cambridge University was closed because of the Plague, and Newton had temporarily withdrawn to his quiet cottage at Woolsthorpe in Lincolnshire. While there, he began the studies which led him on to the theory of gravitation – and, in passing, the story of the tumbling apple is almost certainly true; he really did see an apple fall, and realized that the force which affected the apple was the same as the force which keeps the Moon moving in its path round the Earth. Newton also made some pioneer experiments with sunlight. He passed a beam of light through a glass prism, and noted that the light was spread out into a succession of colours, from red at one end to violet at the other. This showed him that sunlight is made up of all the colours of the rainbow; the various ingredients are bent differently as they pass through the prism. Blue is bent more than red, yellow less than blue, red less than yellow. That was as far as he went, but he had made the essential breakthrough.

We know, as Newton did not, that light may be regarded as a wave motion, and that the colour of the light depends upon its wavelength, i.e. the distance between successive wave-crests. Violet has the shortest wavelength, and is therefore the most strongly bent or refracted as it passes through the prism; red has the longest wavelength, and is refracted the least. By conventional standards, these wavelengths are very tiny. That of red light is about 7,500 Ångströms, while violet goes down to 3,900 Ångströms – and one Ångström is equal to one hundred millionth of a centimetre.* Imagine a line exactly one centimetre long. Try mentally to divide it into 100,000,000 parts, and you will appreciate how small an Ångström is. To the short-wave end of visible light we have ultra-violet, X-rays and the very penetrating gamma-rays; beyond the red we have infra-red and then radio waves. Most people know at least something about these invisible radiations. If you switch on an electric fire, you will feel the infra-red as heat well before the bars start to glow, while X-rays are used every minute in hospitals. Radio waves also come to us from space, though they certainly are not artificial transmissions. All in all, the total range of wavelengths, or 'electromagnetic spectrum', is very extensive.

Matter – all matter; you, me, the Earth, the Sun, the stars and the galaxies – is made up of atoms, which band together to make up atom-groups or molecules. To describe an atom is by no means easy, and in everyday language it simply cannot be done, but I can try to give a general picture. This means repeating a little of what I have said earlier, but atomic studies are so vitally important in any consideration of the Sun's ultimate fate that I make no apology.

To recapitulate, then: in an atom, there is a central nucleus around which revolve particles of lesser mass, rather in the manner of planets moving round the Sun. The nucleus is made up of positively-charged particles (protons) together with particles which have no charge at all (neutrons), while the planetary particles have negative charge (electrons). The nature of the atom depends upon the number of planetary electrons. Thus hydrogen, the simplest and lightest of all the fundamental atom-types or elements, has one electron; helium has two, lithium three, and so on until we reach

---

*The unit is named after the last-century Swedish physicist Anders Ångström, who carried out a great deal of important work. Typists and printers often bemoan the fact that he was inconvenient enough to have a surname beginning with the Swedish letter Å!

uranium, which has 92. There is a complete sequence, and we are sure that no elements have been left out, because one cannot have half an electron. Additional elements, with more than 92 electrons, have been made in our laboratories; these include plutonium, which is excessively dangerous and is used, among other things, in the manufacture of nuclear bombs. But all these extra elements are unstable, and they have not been found in nature.

The difficulty about all this is that we cannot picture a proton, an electron or a neutron as a solid lump. However, this is as far as I propose to go at the moment, and I hope that readers with a sound knowledge of physics will not object too strongly to what I realize is a gross over-simplification.

When the light from an incandescent solid, liquid or high-pressure gas is passed through a prism, or something which acts in the same way, the result is a rainbow band or spectrum. When the light from an incandescent low-pressure gas is examined, there is no band; instead, there are disconnected bright lines, and each line is the trademark of some particular element or molecule. Thus if we see two distinctive yellow lines, we know that they are due to the element sodium, and cannot possibly be caused by anything else. All the natural elements may be identified in this way, though some are much more elusive than others.

In 1814 a young German optician named Josef von Fraunhofer examined the spectrum of the Sun, and noted something very curious. There was a rainbow band, as expected, but crossing it there were dark lines, and these lines never changed their positions or their intensities. Fraunhofer mapped them, and they are still often called the Fraunhofer lines (he was not the first to see them, but he pioneered scientific studies of them). More than 40 years later two of his countrymen, Kirchhoff and Bunsen, found out how the lines are produced, and so opened up the way to modern solar spectroscopy.

The Sun's surface is made up of shining gas, and emits a rainbow or 'continuous' spectrum. Overlying the bright surface is a region of much thinner gases, and these would normally produce bright or 'emission' lines; but because of the rainbow in the background they are 'reversed', i.e. they appear dark. This does not mean that they cannot be identified. For instance, there are two prominent dark lines in the yellow part of the rainbow which correspond to the famous bright lines emitted by sodium, and so we may be sure that there is sodium in the Sun. By now, over 70 of the 92 naturally-occurring elements have been found there.

Of these elements, the most abundant is hydrogen, and indeed the whole universe is rich in hydrogen. In sheer numbers, hydrogen atoms are more plentiful than those of all the other elements put together, and helium comes a poor second. We live, in fact, in a hydrogen-dominated environment, though in our everyday life we are not conscious of it. (Remember, however, that water is made up partly of hydrogen, and the formula H_2O indicates that a water-molecule is composed of two hydrogen atoms together with one atom of oxygen.)

Since the stars are suns, they too would be expected to yield spectra of the same kind – and they do. Things are less easy, because with the Sun there is plenty of light available for analysis, and with the stars we have to collect as much light as possible by using a powerful telescope before passing it through spectroscopic equipment; but the principles are the same, and in the late 19th century some important researches were carried out, notably by an English amateur, William (later Sir William) Huggins and an Italian Jesuit, Angelo Secchi. Their work led on to the first concrete ideas about stellar evolution.

The stars are not alike. With the naked eye it is easy to see that some of them are reddish; Betelgeux in the shoulder of Orion is one example, and Antares in the Scorpion is another, while the brilliant Arcturus in Boötes (the Herdsman), which lies in line with the curve of the Great Bear's tail, is light orange. Vega in Lyra (the Harp or Lyre), which is almost overhead as seen from England during summer evenings, is glorious blue, while Capella in Auriga (the Charioteer), with occupies the overhead position during winter evenings, is yellow like the Sun. In the far south, never visible from anywhere in Europe, we have the famed Southern Cross, which is compact and brilliant, though its shape is more like that of a kite than an X. Of its leaders, three are bluish-white, while the fourth (Gamma Crucis) is red.

Anyone using binoculars, or a telescope, will be able to make out these colours strongly, and fainter stars also show them. Look, for instance, at Mu Cephei, in the far north of the sky; I am afraid you will have to locate it by means of a star map, because it is only dimly visible without optical aid. Telescopically it is seen to glow deep red, which is why Sir William Herschel nicknamed it 'the Garnet Star'.

The different colours indicate differences in surface temperature. This is logical enough; after all, blue heat is hotter than yellow heat, while yellow is hotter than orange or red. The very hottest stars have surface temperatures of well over 40,000 degrees Centigrade, while others range down to below 30,000 degrees for Vega, 10,700 degrees for the pure white Sirius, 6,000 degrees for the Sun and only about 3,400 degrees for Betelgeux, while the reddest of all stars are cooler still. Long ago, astronomers began to feel that these various colours indicated some sort of an evolutionary sequence, and then came another revelation which appeared to put matters upon a really firm footing. This was the discovery that red stars, at least, can be divided into two definite classes: giants and dwarfs.

I must here introduce you to what is known as a Hertzsprung-Russell or H-R Diagram, so named because it was worked out by Ejnar Hertzsprung of Denmark and Henry Norris Russell of the United States. They produced a chart in which the stars were plotted according to their spectral types and their luminosities. As you can see on the diagram facing page 109, most of the stars fall into a line running from the top left down to the bottom right. This line is called the Main Sequence; the selection of stars given here is absolutely typical, and the Sun itself is a normal Main Sequence star. I have also put in the luminosities, taking the Sun as a standard. At the top of the Main Sequence we have bluish-white stars thousands of times more powerful than the Sun, while at the bottom there are Red Dwarfs which may be termed cosmical glow-worms. The feeblest Main Sequence star known, EG 0050 − 2722 in the southern constellation of the Sculptor, has a surface temperature of below 2,700 degrees, and a mass only 20 times that of Jupiter.

But now look at the red stars! There are some which are real searchlights, and lie to the upper right of the H-R Diagram, making up the giant branch; but red stars about equal in luminosity to the Sun do not exist. The difference between giants and dwarfs is less for orange stars and still less for yellow, after which we come to the hot stars which are not sharply separated into distinct grades. (For the moment, let us forget about the White Dwarfs, to the lower left of the diagram. They are very much part of the story, but they come into a different category altogether.)

It may be true to say that the H-R Diagrams are about the most significant astronomical charts ever made, and so far as stellar evolution is concerned we would be lost without them. They led at once to a suggested sequence of events which turned out to be wrong, but which seemed to be eminently reasonable at the time. It was thought that a star began its career by condensing out of one of the nebulæ, or gas-and-dust clouds which I have already mentioned. Initially the star was large, cool and therefore red. As it shrank, under the influence of gravity, it became hotter, turning first yellow and then white. When it reached the top of the Main \ Sequence it would be at the peak of its career, and it would then start to cool off as well as shrinking, becoming in succession a Yellow Dwarf like the Sun, an orange star and then a Red Dwarf, reaching the lower right of the Main Sequence. Finally it would become so cool that it would fade out, ending up as a cold, dead Black Dwarf.

If this picture had been right, then life on Earth would have come to a slow but unpleasant end. As the Sun is now a Yellow Dwarf, it would have passed its peak, and would be slowly cooling down as it shrank. Admittedly the decline would be gradual, but eventually it would make itself felt in no uncertain fashion. The Earth's temperature would fall. The ice-caps at the poles would creep slowly but remorselessly towards the equator; country after country would be covered; and unless some remedy could be found, the habitable parts of the globe would become smaller and smaller until Mankind, or what was left of it, had been forced back to huddle near the equator. Even this would be no more than a temporary respite. As the Sun entered its Red Dwarf phase, the oceans would freeze solid; bitter winds would sweep across the whole world – until at last the temperature became so low that the air itself would turn into first a liquid and then a solid block. By that time no trace of life would be left anywhere on the Earth's surface, and whether the remnants of humanity could survive for long by burrowing underground seems rather improbable. At any rate, the final extinction of life would come well before the last of the Sun's energy sputtered out. All that would be left of the Solar System would be a dark, dead star still orbited by the ghosts of its planets.

Death by creeping cold is not an attractive prospect. However, it will not happen, because modern research has shown that the whole scenario is wrong. The Sun is not cooling down as it ages. We will be destroyed not by being frozen, but by being vaporized.

What set astronomers on the right track was that the whole time-scale of stellar evolution was wrong. If a star evolved in the manner originally supposed, it would be short-lived; yet we know that the Sun is well over 4,000 million years old, and this meant that some other source of energy had to be found. It was next proposed that the star actually annihilated its material, so that it could draw upon the vast reserves locked up inside its atoms. This swung the time-scale too far in the opposite direction. Annihilation could, it was thought, maintain a star for about 10,000,000 million years, which did not agree at all with what we had found about the ages of the Sun and the Earth. Then, in 1939, the vital clue was found, mainly by a German-born astronomer named Hans Bethe, who was living in America. He attended a conference in Washington, and on the train-journey back to Harvard he started 'doodling' on a piece of paper. Before dinner was served, he had worked out the nuclear reactions which can explain most, if not all, of the difficulties.

Again hydrogen is the key. Normal stars, such as the Sun, use it as 'fuel'. The whole process is very complicated, but I do not propose to fog the issue here, so once again I am going to plead guilty to over-simplification, and consider what happens to various types of stars. The entire life-story depends upon the star's initial mass.

Case 1: *stars of very low mass, less than about 1/16 that of the Sun.* After the star has been formed from the nebular material, it starts to contract and heat up inside; but it is so lightweight that the core temperature never becomes high enough for nuclear reactions to begin. Therefore the star does not achieve anything but faint red luminosity, and though it may shine for a long period it then subsides meekly into the Black Dwarf condition.

Case 2: *stars of mass comparable with that of the Sun.* Here we have a very different picture. As the young star shrinks, it starts to shine – jerkily, so that there is considerable irregular variation; this is, of course, the T Tauri condition mentioned earlier. Then, as the core goes on heating up, it reaches the critical value of about 10,000,000 degrees Centigrade, and nuclear reactions are triggered off. Broadly speaking, the hydrogen nuclei start to run together to make up nuclei of Element No. 2, helium. It takes four hydrogen nuclei to make one helium nucleus, and in the process a little energy is set free and a little mass is lost. It is this energy which keeps the star radiating. With the Sun the loss of mass is equal to 4,000,000 tons per second, and the 'weight' of the Sun is much less now than it was when you started to read this page. (Please do not worry; there is plenty left!) The temperature at the star's core rises to around

14,000,000 to 15,000,000 degrees Centigrade, and the star joins the Main Sequence.

This stage in a star's life lasts for a long time. The Sun has been on the Main Sequence for over 4,000 million years, and it has at least an equal period in the future, but eventually the supply of available hydrogen will start to run low, and the Sun will have to rearrange itself. The outer layers will expand and cool, while the core will shrink and heat up. At this stage different reactions are triggered off; helium reacts, and by a whole series of processes heavier and heavier elements are built up. The star leaves the Main Sequence, and enters the giant branch of the H-R Diagram. It has been estimated that 6,000 or 7,000 million years hence, the Sun will have a diameter of at least 100,000,000 miles, and will send out 100 times as much energy as it does now, despite its cooler surface.

The Red Giant stage is relatively brief. As the Sun evolves, it will throw off its outer parts, creating what is termed a planetary nebula – a bad term, because an object of this sort is not truly a nebula, and is most certainly not a planet. The thrown-off shell will expand and escape into space, while what is left of the Sun will collapse. It will become very small and incredibly dense, because its constituent nuclei will be crushed together with hardly any waste of space. The Sun will become a White Dwarf.

You can see now why I put White Dwarfs into a special category. They are bankrupt, and nothing lies ahead of them but death, though they can continue shining very feebly for thousands of millions of years before they lose the last of their light and heat. Their densities may reach 200,000 times that of water, so that a thimbleful of White Dwarf material would weigh tons. The best-known White Dwarf is the companion of the brilliant Sirius; it is 26,000 miles in diameter, smaller than a planet such as Uranus or Neptune, but its mass is about the same as that of the Sun. Other even more extreme examples are known, some of them even smaller than the Moon.

I hope you will now appreciate why I have taken so long to come to the point! The Earth cannot survive the Sun's Red Giant stage, and this will be the way in which our world really will perish, but for the moment let us complete the story by describing the remaining categories.

Case 3: *stars considerably more massive than the Sun.* With a mass more than about 1.4 times that of the Sun, everything is accelerated. As before, we have the contraction stage, a highly-luminous Main Sequence stage and a Red Giant (or supergiant) stage, but the time-scale is much shorter than with a mild star such as the Sun, and instead of staying at its peak for thousands of millions of years it may run through its reserves in less than a million years. Consider a star such as S Doradûs, which lies in the southern star-system known as the Large Cloud of Magellan. Its luminosity is approximately a million times that of the Sun; it is squandering its 'fuel' at a furious rate, and on the cosmical scale disaster lies close ahead. Eta Carinæ, referred to earlier, is in even greater danger.

When the collapse starts, things become 'out of control', so to speak, and the star explodes in a cataclysmic outburst; it becomes a supernova. The explosion is fatal. Much of the star's material is blown away, and the remnant sinks down into a tiny, super-dense object made of neutrons – produced when the protons and electrons are forced together, so that their electrical charges cancel each other out. $(+ 1 - 1 = 0.)$ A neutron star is indeed a fascinating object. The diameter may be no more than a few miles, but the density rises to a 100,000,000 million times that of water.

The story of the discovery of neutron stars is of such interest that I cannot refrain from saying something about it here, even though since the Sun is not massive enough to form a neutron star, it is rather outside our main theme. In 1967 astronomers at Cambridge University were studying radio waves from space which, as we have seen, are electromagnetic vibrations of long wavelength. A member of the team, Miss Jocelyn Bell (now Dr Jocelyn Bell-Burnell) detected a discrete radio source which was fluctuating so rapidly, and so regularly, that for a short, hectic period it was even thought that the signals might be artificial. Finally, it was decided that the source was a rapidly-rotating neutron star or 'pulsar', associated with an amazingly strong magnetic field.

Other pulsar discoveries followed, and one was found inside the Crab Nebula which, as we have seen, is the wreck of the 1054 supernova. Subsequently the Crab pulsar was identified with a very faint optical object, flashing 30 times every second. This was the first neutron star to be actually seen, and even today there is only one other, discovered in 1977 by astronomers at the Siding Spring Observatory in Australia; it lies in the southern constellation of Vela (the Sails). The rest are known only because of their radio emissions.

117

To account for the quick-fire 'flashes', it has been found that the energy is being sent out in preferential directions; there are two beams, and each time the Earth passes through a beam we receive a pulse of radio energy and, in the case of the Crab and Vela pulsars, an optical flash as well. The effect is rather like that of a rotating lighthouse.

It has also been found that pulsars are definitely gradually slowing down, so that they are losing their energy. The Crab is a good example; it seems that the period will double in about 1,200 years from now. In the long run all pulsars will lose their energy, and we will be left with super-dense, super-massive corpses.

Case 4: *stars of still higher mass*. Here we enter the realms of speculation and uncertainty, and I will be brief, because we are even further removed from the fate of the Sun and the Earth. When the grand collapse starts, gravitation takes over, and no supernova outburst has the chance to happen. The star goes on getting smaller and smaller, denser and denser. As it does so, its escape velocity increases. When even light can no longer break free, it becomes a Black Hole.

I have mentioned Black Holes before, in connection with the suggestion that there may be one wandering in the outskirts of the Solar System, but generally our only hope of detecting them is to see how they affect visible objects near them. Probably the best case is that of Cygnus X-1, which consists of a massive star attended by an invisible companion with a mass 15 times that of the Sun, well into the Black Hole range. As material spirals downwards into the Black Hole, it is violently heated, and emits X-rays of very short wavelength – hence the designation Cygnus X-1.

Let us admit that the existence of Black Holes has not been conclusively proved. As theoretical possibilities they have been discussed for a long time (as far back as the 1930s), but not all astronomers are happy about them, and neither can we have much idea of conditions inside one of them. The ordinary laws of common sense break down, and it may even be that the collapsed star crushes itself out of existence altogether. This in turn leads on to exotic theories according to which it might be possible to enter a Black Hole and emerge unscathed in some other part of the universe, or even in a different universe . . . I must be frank, and say that I have grave misgivings about this sort of thing, but I must not digress any longer, intriguing though the whole subject is.

Now let us sum matters up, and see what we can find out with regard to the eventual fate of the Earth.

All the researches carried out during the past few decades lead us to believe that our ideas about the past and future of the Sun are more or less correct. We may be wrong in detail but not, I think, about the basic principles: birth by contraction from interstellar material, the start of nuclear reactions, the conversion from hydrogen to helium, the Main Sequence period now in progress, the Red Giant stage, collapse to a White Dwarf, and final death as a cold, dead globe. There is absolutely no fear of a supernova outburst, because the Sun is not nearly massive enough, and even less chance of a collapse into a Black Hole. So far as the time-scale is concerned – well, I have given 5,000 million years hence for the start of the change from a Main Sequence star into a giant, but this may be too pessimistic, and figures of 6,000 to 7,000 million years have been given. What is virtually certain is that no dramatic change will take place *before* 5,000 million years in the future. This is not to suggest that things will stay just as they are. The Sun may well be the cause of the ice ages, and it is perfectly capable of causing another; a comparatively slight change in solar output could have devastating results, and Mankind would be hard pressed to cope with them. If the temperature dropped to the level of the period before 8000 BC we would certainly survive, though the world population would be reduced. If the climate became markedly warmer, then again we would manage, though it might mean abandoning the equatorial regions and migrating towards the poles. All this, of course, is little more than guesswork, and there is no evidence that any alteration is imminent. In any case, life would persist, always assuming that there were no complicating factors.

Since we have ruled out the possibility of the Sun turning into a nova, we are left with its eventual transformation into a Red Giant. This not only *may* happen; it *will* happen. How humanity will react is something which we cannot foresee. If we have survived as a race, and put away our atom bombs, there is always the chance that we will have learned enough to achieve interstellar travel, in which event the obvious course would be mass emigration to a planet moving round a more accommodating star. When the Sun swells out, there can be no hope for the innermost planets, Mercury and Venus, and very little for the Earth. At best, our oceans will boil away, the atmosphere will be driven off, and the end product will be

119

a scorched, barren, airless and lifeless globe. It is much more likely that the Earth will be vaporized altogether. The outer planets may survive, and I suppose we might consider migrating to their satellites, such as the four Galilean moons of Jupiter and perhaps Titan and other members of Saturn's family, but this would be a temporary measure only, since the giant stage in the Sun will be succeeded by collapse into a White Dwarf with a tiny fraction of the present-day luminosity. Also, these satellites could not take more than a few per cent of the Earth's present population, though unless something is done about the birth-rate long before then we will have a major crisis on our hands in any case.

Five thousand million years is a long time, bearing in mind that what we call modern civilization has not yet lasted for as long as 5,000 years. Moreover, there will be plenty of warning. Assuming that we have continued to progress and prosper, astronomers will start to see the danger-signals at an early stage. There will be thousands of years to prepare, and perhaps as long as several millions. Flight from the Earth? Methods of driving the world into a new orbit, further from the Sun and therefore beyond the danger-zone? Some way of modifying the Earth itself, so that we can dispense with the energy sent out by the Sun? This is sheer fantasy, but it is inevitable that the period of intense heat will be succeeded by one of numbing cold.

I do not think that we can profitably pursue the subject any further, because we have so little to guide us, but at least we have decided upon the real fate of the Earth. Life here will not be slowly frozen as the Sun fades, as used to be thought. The end will come by a steady increase of heat, until our present gentle, yellow Sun becomes a sinister red agent of destruction.

At least we have the satisfaction of knowing that you and I won't be there.

Chapter Ten

Do it Yourself!

So far as natural causes are concerned, the end of the world is not imminent. Until the Sun starts to show signs of senility we should be reasonably safe from all cosmic threats. However, there is one other threat which cannot be ignored, and it comes from ourselves. Can we take any action which will destroy the Earth?

It would be easy enough to wipe out civilization, and indeed all life on Earth. It could be accomplished in a few hours by weapons already stockpiled in the Kremlin, the White House and perhaps elsewhere, and it has been well within the bounds of possibility ever since the Hiroshima bomb of 1945. There is also chemical warfare, and various other unpleasant procedures have also been mooted, such as bombs which kill people and animals, leaving masonry almost untouched. I do not want to stray into the murky realm of politics, but I do sometimes wonder whether any allegedly intelligent race which can even contemplate this sort of thing deserves to survive, and moreover, looking around at the present leaders of the nations inspires me with no confidence at all. It is also sadly true that we can expect no major war between the great races to be fought only with what are termed conventional weapons, because nuclear bombs would be used eventually by whichever side happened to be losing. What we must decide, then, is: can any future conflict wipe out the Earth as well as its inhabitants?

A nuclear explosion is probably the only way, and it would have to be let off either on the Earth's surface or below it. Of course, those who watched and enjoyed the film *Star Wars* (as I did) will remember how a whole planet was annihilated by a death-ray aimed at it by Lord Darth Vader, but this seems very far-fetched. Such a ray could be produced, I suppose; but any race advanced enough to develop it would certainly have the sense not to do so.

Many people have maintained that even at the present time the worst dangers of all come from space weapons, and I remember one article, written around 1960, in which it was said that whoever controlled the Moon would also control the Earth. Yet this makes no sense at all. It is true that spy-satellites exist, and are being regularly used for reconnaissance, but the Moon is a very different matter, and future lunar stations will surely be purely scientific. They may even be of real help in other ways, because they will be operated not by politicians, but by scientists actually on the spot, which may lead to real international collaboration. There can be no chance of a lunar Darth Vader setting out to eliminate the Earth and everybody on it. We come back, then, to the prospect of a fatal nuclear explosion at or below ground level.

Nuclear bombs now exist which would make those dropped on Hiroshima and Nagasaki look like squibs, but even if all of them were exploded at once the jolt would be too slight to alter the tilt of the axis, or to disrupt the Earth completely. However, the crust might well be broken, resulting in major earthquakes and colossal outpourings of lava; tidal waves would devastate the lands, and the atmosphere would also be affected, since it would probably become so intensely radioactive that no life could survive even if it managed to come through the initial shock. But it could not achieve global destruction, and neither could it change the Earth's path round the Sun to any measurable extent.

The existence of the Earth cannot therefore be imperilled by anything that Man can do. Its nature could be altered, and it could be transformed into a sterile, radioactive waste which would be permanently uninhabitable, but it would still exist. Excluding any wildly improbable natural mishap, it will continue in its orbit until the final crisis comes, when both it and any remaining life are swept away in the unbelievable blaze that will announce the Sun's departure from the Main Sequence. From this, there can be no escape.

Chapter Eleven

Aftermath

There are two vital questions which remain to be answered. We know that the Earth must die eventually, but does this mean that all life in the universe will become extinct? Secondly, will the universe itself come to an end?

Up to now I have been talking mainly about the Solar System, that cosmic village which is ruled by the Sun and of which the Earth is a minor though unique member. The Solar System is contained in the Galaxy, a vast assemblage of around 100,000 million stars, some of which are much older than others; star formation is still going on in nebulæ such as that in Orion's Sword. There is a great deal of interstellar material which has not yet been used up, so that the Galaxy is still in its prime.

Before the 1920s it was generally believed that our Galaxy was the only one, but there were doubts about it, and these had been expressed by Sir William Herschel much earlier. Not all the so-called nebulæ are of the same type as Orion's Sword. Others give every impression of being made up of stars, and in 1845 that amazing amateur, the Earl of Rosse, completed a telescope powerful enough to show that some of these objects are spiral. For instance, the so-called Whirlpool, in the little constellation of the Hunting Dogs, lives up to its name. The brightest of the 'starry nebulæ' visible from Europe is also a spiral, though it is placed at an awkward angle to us and the full beauty is lost. It lies in the constellation of Andromeda, and is just visible with the naked eye as a misty blur. It is known officially as M.31, because it was the 31st object in a catalogue of star-clusters and nebulæ drawn up by Charles Messier, a French contemporary of Herschel's.

Herschel made the vague suggestion that M.31 and others of its kind might be separate galaxies – independent 'star cities', lying far beyond the confines of our own. He was quite unable to give any proof (remember, in his day no star-distance had been measured), and he kept a completely open mind, but it was a bold guess. Subsequently it was more or less discredited, and was dismissed as a half-forgotten speculation, but it came to the fore again following some outstanding work by an American woman astronomer, Henrietta Leavitt, just before World War I.

In the far south of the sky there are two objects known as the Magellanic Clouds, or Clouds of Magellan, because they were described by the Portuguese explorer Ferdinand Magellan during his round-the-world voyage which began in 1519. Actually they must have been seen much earlier than that, because they are easily visible with the naked eye, and to the casual onlooker they resemble broken-off parts of the Milky Way; but it was always obvious that they were something special, and when astronomical photography became a powerful means of investigation they were carefully studied. At Harvard, in the United States, Miss Leavitt took a long, hard look at the pictures of them which had been sent to her from Harvard Observatory's southern station in Peru. In the Clouds she detected some stars which did not shine steadily as most stars do; they brightened and faded over short periods of a few days, and they were completely regular in their behaviour. Variable stars of this kind were already known in our Galaxy, and were called Cepheids, because the best-known member of the class is Delta Cephei.

Miss Leavitt found that the Cepheids with the longer periods – that is to say, those which took a greater time to pass from one maximum to the next – looked more brilliant than those with shorter periods. Now, since the Clouds are so far away, all the stars in them can be regarded as equally distant. The rule of 'the brighter, the slower' held good for all the Cepheids in the Small Magellanic Cloud upon which Miss Leavitt concentrated, and this was of tremendous importance, because it followed that the Cepheids which looked the brighter were genuinely the more luminous. The same rule was valid for the Cepheids in other parts of the sky, some of which, including Delta Cephei itself, are easily visible with the naked eye.

If it is possible to find the real luminosity of a Cepheid merely by following its changes in brightness, we have an immediate clue to its distance. Take two Cepheids, one with a period of five days and the other with a period of seven days. If they look equally brilliant, then

ABOVE: *The War of the Worlds* panic; Americans, still in their night clothes, do their best to evade the 'Martians' described in the radio broadcast of H. G. Wells' novel.

BELOW: The 'Big Bang'. Suddenly, and for reasons so far totally unknown, the universe comes into existence with a blaze which would make the most powerful supernova seem like a squib.

The Earth's fate is sealed; the Sun has begun to turn into a Red Giant, and the blaze of heat means that neither Earth nor any other of the inner planets can survive.

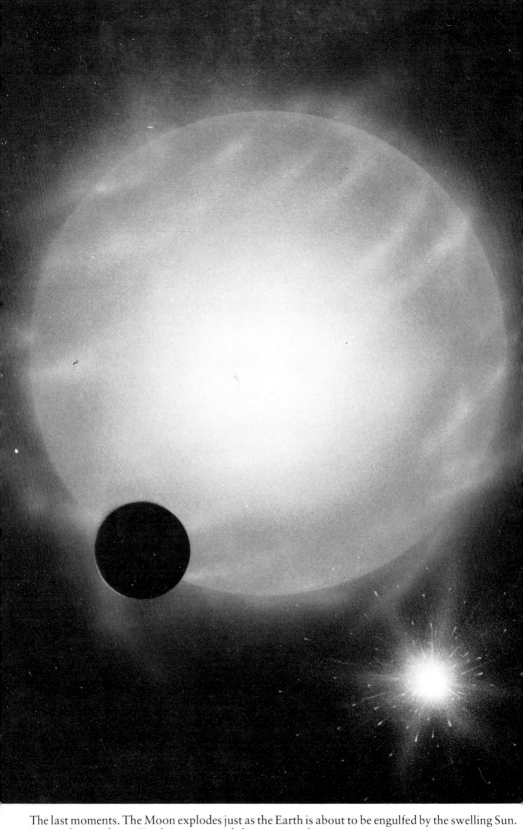

The last moments. The Moon explodes just as the Earth is about to be engulfed by the swelling Sun.
Doomsday, so far as Earth is concerned, has come at last.

the seven-day star must be the further away, because it is the more powerful (I am here ignoring complications such as the dimming of light by interstellar dust). Cepheids could be used as 'standard candles' in space, and because they are highly luminous they can be seen across vast distances.

The problem was taken up by another American, Edwin Hubble, who had the advantage of being able to use what was then the largest telescope in the world: the 100-inch reflector at Mount Wilson in California, completed in 1917. Hubble took photographs of M.31 and other spirals, and found Cepheids in them. He could then determine the periods of the Cepheids, find their distances, and hence the distances of the spirals in which they lay. All doubts were banished: the 'starry nebulæ' were so remote that they could not possibly be members of our Galaxy. Herschel's hesitant guess had been proved right after all.

M.31 is now known to be 2,200,000 light-years away.* The Clouds of Magellan are closer, at less than 200,000 light-years, and there are other galaxies making up what we call the Local Group. Not all are spiral; some are elliptical, and some have no definite shape at all, but all seem to be of the same basic nature. M.31 is the senior member of the Local Group, and is larger than our Galaxy, with at least 150,000 million stars. But even this was only a beginning; most of the galaxies were far outside the Local Group, at distances of many millions of light-years.

The Cepheids can extend our surveys out to over 40,000,000 light-years, but then they are lost in the general background glow, and other methods have to take over. In the meantime, another remarkable discovery had been made. Excluding the members of the Local Group, all the galaxies are moving away from us, and the further away they are the faster they go. In fact, the whole universe is expanding.

The clue here was given by the spectroscope. I hope you remember how a star's spectrum is formed; there is a rainbow background, crossed by dark lines characteristic of individual

---

*This is further than Hubble's original estimate of less than 1,000,000 light years. In 1952 the German astronomer Walter Baade, working with the Palomar 200-inch reflector, found that there had been an error in the Cepheid scale, and that the universe was larger than had been believed – a trifling error of approximately 100 per cent!

atoms or molecules. Galaxies show spectra made up of the combined light of millions of stars, and they are bound to be something of a jumble, but the main lines can be identified, and they were found to be shifted away from their normal positions. This was explained as being due to the Doppler effect, so named in honour of the Austrian physicist Christian Doppler, who first drew attention to it as long ago as 1842. If a light-source is receding, all the lines in the spectrum are moved over towards the long-wave or red end of the rainbow band. This is the celebrated Red Shift; and the amount of the Red Shift gives a key to the velocity of recession.

Photographs of the spectra of galaxies left little room for doubt; and though many attempts have been made to explain the Red Shifts in some alternative way, no other explanation has been successful. According to all the current evidence, the expansion of the universe is real. There is a well-defined law (Hubble's Law) which links distance with recessional velocity, and this can be used to extend our measurements still further. Once we know the amount of Red Shift, we can estimate how fast that particular galaxy is racing away, and hence we can obtain its distance. By now we have reached out to thousands of millions of light-years, involving recessional velocities which are almost incredibly great.

Radio telescopes also come into the story, because the Doppler shifts affect radio waves too. Since 1963 much has been heard of 'quasars', which seem to be much smaller than normal galaxies but also much more luminous and remote. ('Quasar' is a convenient abbreviation for 'quasi-stellar' radio source; note that there is no connection between a quasar, which is far outside our Galaxy, and a pulsar, which is comparatively local even though one has recently been discovered in the Large Cloud of Magellan.) If the Red Shifts are not misleading us, then some of the quasars are the most remote objects known to us. One, PKS 2000-330, identified by Australian astronomers in 1982, appears to be at least 13,000 million light-years away from us, and is receding at well over 90 per cent of the velocity of light.

If Hubble's Law remains valid at still greater distances, we will eventually come to a point at which a galaxy (or a quasar) is speeding away at the full velocity of light. In this case we will be unable to see it, and we will have reached the edge of the observable universe, though not necessarily the limit of the universe itself. According to recent estimates, the critical distance may be around

15,000 million light-years, though different authorities have rather different ideas about it.

We can also calculate in reverse, so to speak. Assuming that the expansion has always been at the same rate as it is now, we can estimate that it must have begun 15,000 million years ago, in which case the universe is approximately three times as old as the Earth. But how did the universe come into being? And more importantly still in our present context, how will it end?

The favoured theory at the present time is known commonly as the Big Bang. This assumes that all the matter in the universe came into being at one definite moment in time, in the form of a 'primæval atom'; this primæval atom exploded, so that material spread outwards to form galaxies, then stars and then, in many cases planetary systems. The expansion will continue indefinitely, so that in the long run each group of galaxies will lose contact with each other group. Stars will die; others will be reborn from the remaining interstellar matter; but this cannot go on for ever, and the end product is a totally cold, dead, dark universe.

A noble but, alas, unsuccessful challenge to the Big Bang was made in the late 1940s by two astronomers at Cambridge University, Thomas Gold and Herman Bondi, who proposed an entirely new theory in which the universe has always existed, and will exist for eternity. As old galaxies vanish over the observable limit, they will be replaced by new ones formed from matter which is created spontaneously out of nothingness. Of course the rate of creation must be much too slow to be detectable, but there is plenty of room, so that from this point of view the theory cannot be attacked, but unfortunately it has been found to have so many other flaws that almost all astronomers have now consigned it to the scientific scrapheap. Rather later came the Oscillating or Cyclic universe, which I irreverently term the concertina universe. If it is correct, the present phase of expansion will not be permanent, and after a while the galaxies will start to draw together again, finally meeting up to produce another Big Bang. It has been suggested that the interval between successive bangs is of the order of 80,000 million years.

This theory depends upon the average density of material spread through the universe. If the density is above a certain critical value, there will be enough gravitational pull to tug the flying galaxies back before they can escape; if the density is too low, this cannot happen, and we are back to the original 'evolutionary' picture. At the moment it looks rather as though the density is insufficient, in which case the concertina theory is wrong, but the last word has by no means been said. There may be a tremendous amount of unknown mass locked up here and there – in Black Holes, for instance.

Another novel idea has been put forward by the eminent Swedish scientist Hannes Alfvén, who has suggested that there may be whole galaxies which are made up of matter of a type fundamentally opposite to our own, so that collision between anti-matter and ordinary matter would mean the instant annihilation of both. This is not impossible, but we have to admit that the evidence is nil, and the concept remains nothing more than fascinating speculation.

All this is very interesting, but I suggest that we are merely skating round the basic problem. Just how did the material making up the universe come into existence in the first place? This is a question which nobody (except the Biblical Fundamentalists) has attempted to answer, and neither are we any better off when we consider the time-scale. If the universe began at a set moment, what happened before that? Yet if we follow the cyclic picture, and assume that there have been many Big Bangs in the past, we are faced with the problem of understanding a period of time that had no beginning. Our brains are unequal to the task, and the question itself may be regarded as unfair. It is four-dimensional, and we are three-dimensional beings – which is another way of saying that I have no clue as to the answer!

Therefore, what we are discussing is not the origin of the universe, but its evolution, which is a different thing. Moreover, how big is space? It may be 'finite but unbounded', though to put this into everyday language defeats me, and has, I claim, defeated every other writer as well.

I have called this chapter 'Aftermath', and surely we are entitled to speculate about what will happen after the end of the Earth. Will our remote descendants succeed in emigrating? If so, they will make a new home on some other planet of some other star; but this star also must die eventually, so that there will have to be a further move. We can even let our imaginations run riot, and visualize intelligent beings travelling desperately from one dying system to another until they are faced with the stark realization that the universe itself has reached its last stages. Yet can there be any chance of a reprieve in some manner quite beyond our understanding? It must be possible, but we have no present hope of finding out.

I have done my best to present you with a balanced picture of what lies in store for us. We have looked at the religious fanatics such as William Miller, the astrologers and other eccentrics, the scares due to comets and asteroids, Orson Welles' Martians and Herr Hörbiger's icy moon; we have entered the fascinating realm of flying saucers, and we have returned to sober science to discuss the eventual death of the Sun. We have also allowed ourselves a final digression to see what will happen to the universe. And the conclusions we reach? The Earth itself is in no danger, and will continue in its path until the Sun wipes it out, which will not occur for at least 5,000 million years. Life could be destroyed by our own folly, but there is a chance that we will come to our senses in time.

Make no mistake about it: the world will come to an end one day. But not yet.

Index